Allan S. Anderson
from Grannie
Xmas 1953.

TALES OF SCOTTISH KEEPS AND CASTLES

WHEN HE WAS WRESTLING WITH IT, ONE OF ITS HORNS CAME OFF IN HIS HANDS

[Page 132

TALES OF SCOTTISH KEEPS & CASTLES

BY

ELIZABETH W. GRIERSON

With eight illustrations in colour
by ALLAN STEWART

ADAM AND CHARLES BLACK
4, 5 AND 6 SOHO SQUARE, LONDON, W. 1

FIRST PUBLISHED 1928
REPRINTED 1933 AND 1948

MADE IN GREAT BRITAIN

CONTENTS

LIST OF ILLUSTRATIONS
(*IN COLOUR*)
By Allan Stewart

TALES OF SCOTTISH KEEPS AND CASTLES

I

OUTWITTED

" Your Majesty is early afoot this morning. Is it a birthday or some Saint's Day that hath called thee from thy bed a good hour sooner than usual? By the arm of St. Geille neither Saint's Day nor birthday would rouse me at six of the clock if I had the soft couch and downy pillows that I have seen in your Highness's chamber."

With these words old Peter Rintoul, one of the soldiers on guard at the Royal Castle of Edinburgh, lowered his pike to the ground, and crossing his hands on its shaft, gazed, with a twinkle in his eye, at a little boy of about eight years old, who was jumping restlessly up and down on one of the rough outcrops of rock which to this day find a place round the buildings of the massive fortress. The child was evidently of noble birth. His doublet of rich white satin, his crimson velvet breeches and silken hose, the jewelled buckles on his cap and shoon, all pointed to wealth and position. And there was something in his bearing—in the way his blue eyes flashed, and the little toss he gave to his long fair curls, that betokened that he was no ordinary child.

He had a pleasant, open face, and would have been very handsome were it not for a bright scarlet mark on one of his cheeks. This mark had not come as the result of an accident, it had been there when he was born, and because of it he bore a nickname which will last as long as Scottish history lasts. For this boy was no other than King James II. of Scotland, "James of the Fiery Face."

As Peter spoke he stopped his restless dancing, and ran up to the old man, pretending to strike him for his teasing words.

" Shame on thee, talking like that!" he cried, " when thou knowest that my birthday fell last January, and that I never go to Mass on Saints' Days till eight on the clock. But thou art just mocking me, Peter Rintoul, and thou hast no right to do so seeing I am thy King. Nay ; but I rose early because I could not sleep for thinking of my Lady Mother, who is coming today to see me, and to stay in the Castle for a whole long week. I have not seen her for two whole years, not since——
And the child turned away proudly, not to let the old soldier see the tears which had suddenly risen

to his eyes, and which threatened to overflow and roll down his face.

Peter Rintoul knew what the boy was thinking about. He knew what a happy childhood he had had, brought up among a merry family of sisters and watched over tenderly by a father and mother who had more culture and refinement than was usual even among people of high rank in Scotland in those days. For his father, King James I., had spent his youth in captivity at the English Court, and had met, at Windsor Castle, the fair Lady Jane Beaufort, whom he had afterwards married. And when the young man regained his liberty and brought his bride home to his northern kingdom, the Royal pair brought there many of the kindlier and gentler customs of the south.

Then, just two years before the time of which our story tells, a dreadful thing had happened.

The King and Queen went with their younger children to spend Christmas at the Grayfriars Monastery at Perth, leaving their eldest son with his tutor at Edinburgh Castle. Alas! the child never saw his father again. Every reader of history knows what happened. How the gay, debonair King was murdered one night by a band of discontented nobles, who rushed into his private apartments in the monastery, and, pursuing him into a cellar, stabbed him to death. No wonder tears rose in the little boy's eyes as he thought of the miserable time that followed. Of the dreary day when his mother came back to the Castle, no longer smiling and gay, but with such a white face and such wild eyes, that her little son shrank in terror from the sight of her. Then followed a time of confusion, when crowds of great bearded men in armour arrived, who, he was told, were his nobles, who ordered him about, and spoke none too kindly to his mother, and would not let him be with her, but put him on a horse, and took him down through the crowded " Hie Street," and along the " gait " or path of the canons to the great abbey church at Holyrood, where they crowned him, and afterwards knelt to kiss his hand and swore allegiance to him.

But their allegiance seemed to end there, or so it appeared to his childish mind, for when they had brought him back to the Castle again, they handed him over to the care of Sir William Crichton, the Chancellor of Scotland, who lived in the fortress, and then they all rode away to their homes. Even his mother went away and left him, for she did not like Sir William, but chose to retire with her younger children to Stirling, which was held by her friend Sir Alexander Livingstone, Governor of Scotland. She would have taken the little King with her if she could. But that was not allowed.

The Chancellor's party was in power, and they were determined to have the keeping of the Royal boy in their own hands. So little James had been practically a prisoner for two years, and although he was kindly treated, and every care taken of him, he was never allowed to set foot outside the precincts of the Castle, but had to play his games and take what exercise he could within its somewhat cramped courtyards and enclosures.

"Now, by'r Lady, but that is a fine prospect!" said old Peter cheerily. "No wonder I heard Sir William giving orders last night to have the tapestry hung out in the chamber that adjoins your Majesty's, and rugs laid on the floor, and gay bunting carried down to the Inner Barrier. And methought there was an extra stir in the kitchen as I passed an hour ago. Doubtless there will be a great supper to-night, and I warrant your Highness will sit up for it. The Queen, thy mother, will rejoice to see how thou hast grown, and in what a kingly manner thou carriest thyself."

The cloud lifted from the little boy's face at the kindly words, and he turned round with a beaming smile.

"Dost thou think I look like a King, Peter?" he cried. "Will I look as noble a King as did my father when I am man-grown?"

"Aye, that wilt thou, my liege," said the old man

proudly, " gin thou attendest to thy tutor, and have in mind always the kingly virtues of truth and honour and justice. But hark ! there is Master Thomas Kincaid calling for thee. 'Tis time to break thy fast; then must thou dress thyself in thy bravest finery, for I heard Sir William say that the Queen's Highness might be expected at the gate by twelve on the clock."

With a shout of delight the boy dashed away, and the faithful old soldier looked after him wistfully with a little shake of his old grizzled head.

" Poor bairn," he muttered, " he hath a dangerous road before him ere he reaches man's estate, which pray God he may. But with party warring against party, with him as the prize, much might happen by that time. 'Tis a mercy his mother is to be allowed to see him at last. To my notion she should be with him always. But that doth not seem to suit the mind of my Lord the Chancellor, who doubtless would lose some of his importance if the laddie were taken out of his keeping."

A few hours later the sound of bugles was heard coming from the direction of the steep, narrow High Street. Everyone except the Chancellor and his Royal ward hastened to the great gateway, and there, wending its way across the open green which lay between the Castle and the Linen Market, was a small but stately procession. There were

about the murder of the late King, gave the sign hastily that all should rise from the table, and, forgetting his manners for the moment, replied rather sharply to the little King's excited entreaties that he might be allowed to accompany his mother on these expeditions.

"Na, na, your Highness," he said. "My orders are to keep ye in this Castle, and it is my job to see that they are obeyed. Now do not yammer about the matter, for it will serve you naught. Scotland hath had enough mischief over Kings who were young enough to steal, without me allowing a loop-hole for any such a ploy."

He glanced at Queen Jane as he uttered these words, wondering how she would take this re-minder that her son was virtually a prisoner, and that she could not take him about with her as she chose; but to his surprise her face was quite com-posed and calm, and there was even a twinkle of amusement in her blue eyes, as, stretching out her hand in a friendly way, she bade him good-night.

"The fool, little did he think he was playing into my hands with his silly up-starting pride," she said to one of her ladies, " putting me in my place, by showing me I could not do what I like with my own bairn, while all the time he was just making the poor little lad discontented by showing him that as long as he is here there is never a chance of him having either pony or jennet, or of learning to ride like other boys of his age. Well, my little King will be all the more ready to summon his courage and fall in with our plan when we have prepared his mind and the time comes for us to tell him about it."

Even in the light of what followed, Sir William Crichton, who was a truthful man, could never hide from himself how much he enjoyed that week. For he rode hither and thither at the right hand of the Queen, revelling in the dignity and importance of it all. For, as was fitting, her Majesty was always attended by a small retinue, and the townsfolk, and those living in the country also, assembled in crowds and in little companies to see them and to cheer as they rode along. As for the boy King, it could not be helped that he cried when they rode away, leaving him behind with his tutor and old Peter Rintoul. He had his duty to the country, as well as to himself, and that duty demanded that the bairn should be kept safe behind strong walls and locked gates. So Sir William Crichton, Chancellor of Scotland, quieted his conscience and managed to enjoy his unwonted junketing with a fair and winsome lady at the same time.

One wonders what he would have thought could he have heard some of the conversations that took place between mother and son when the Queen returned from one or other of her outings. Taking the little boy on her knee, she would sit at her open window, from which could be seen the wooded country that stretched down to the sparkling waters of the Firth of Forth and the kingdom of Fife behind it. She would whisper to him her sympathy and indignation because he had no pony to ride like other boys, and stir up his discontent by descriptions of the lovely, wide-spreading Park at Stirling Castle, where boys as young as he were already being trained to hunt and hawk and ride at the ring.

" Couldst thou not take me with thee, mother ?" pleaded the little fellow one evening. " 'Tis lonesome here. For though Peter Rintoul is oh ! so good to me, and makes me a target at which to let fly my arrows, and even shoots along with me sometimes, 'tis not like having a playmate of my own age, like as thou sayest the son of the Governor at Stirling hath."

" I would take thee gladly, my son," replied his mother, " for I trow thou wouldst be happier at Stirling than here; but I have my Lord Chancellor to reckon with, and thou hast heard what he says. He will not even allow thee to go into the good town of Edinburgh, where the citizens would gladly die for thee. He pretends that it is for thine own sake and thy safe keeping. But I know better. 'Tis solely for his own greed and his own party. For thou art the King of Scotland, my lamb, and whoever hath thee in his hands holds the reins of power."

"But, mother, could I not steal out hidden under thy cloak, or couldst thou not let me down from this window in a basket, like as Abbot John says they did to the holy St. Paul? Abbot John comes from Holyrood every week, as thou knowest, to teach me my Credo and the doctrines of the Church. Do not tell anyone, mother, else would they be angry; but when I am alone I often look over the Forth, and pretend to myself how I will escape some day, and, disguised as a beggar boy, walk all the way to Stirling." Though he pretended to laugh at his own fancies, there was a quiver in the little King's voice, as he laid his head against her shoulder, that showed his mother how lonely and homesick he must sometimes be.

"Listen, sweetheart," she said, lifting him up, big boy as he was, on to her knee, and laying her head so close to his that the words she whispered in his ear could not have been heard by anyone else. "I can take thee with me if thou art brave enough to do exactly what I tell thee, and to endure a very uncomfortable journey, completely in the dark."

"Oh, mother!" cried the boy, jumping up in

such excitement that his mother was fain to lay her hand firmly on his mouth to check the words that would have come tumbling out, and which, if they had been overheard, would have upset all her plans.

" Come now, rattle-pate," she said, for she saw the danger into which the boy's excitement might lead her. " I thought I was speaking to a man, I fear me thou art nought but a great senseless bairn." The reproof brought the colour to the little King's face.

" I forgot, mother," he said penitently, " for the thought of going with thee made me feel quite daft. But I will be quite quiet now, and will not ask thee another question—but just do what I am told, so long as thou dost not leave me behind."

" That is my brave son," said his mother, kissing him. " Now I feel that I am once more speaking to a man. See—this is my plan. Thou knowest these great coffers, four of them, which my ladies and I brought along with us, filled with our dresses and our stuff. Supposing that when we go out of the Castle our robes and our fal-dals be a trifle tighter packed than they were when we came, and that they filled only three boxes, and that the fourth contained——"

" *Me!*" interrupted the King solemnly under his

breath, a red spot rising on each cheek and his eyes shining with excitement.

" Aye, just thee," replied his mother, " wrapped all round in a blanket to prevent thee being rattled about and knocked black and blue when the servants are handling the box, and with plenty of air-holes all about thee, to make sure that thou art not smoored* on the road. I think it might be managed, Jimmie, if thou art a brave lad, and after all it would not be for very long, for we would let thee out as soon as we got thee on board the ship at Leith. Dost thou think thou dare face it, my son ?"

" Oh, mother !" said the boy, speaking as earnestly and gravely as if he had, in the last hour, added a couple of years to his age, " just try me. I'll never say a word about it, and when thou hast gotten me in the box, I'll be as quiet as a wee, wee mouse. I'll never play cheep, even if they turn the box on end so that I am standing upside down."

In the gray light of the second morning after this conversation had taken place, the Queen and her ladies were early afoot, for it had been arranged that their boat should set sail by the first tide, so it was necessary that they should be down at Leith by seven o'clock in the morning. Her Majesty had taken an affectionate farewell of her son the night

* Smothered.

before, and had asked the Chancellor to give orders that he was not to be disturbed next morning, but was to be allowed to " get his sleep out," so that the travellers would be gone before he awoke and he would not be upset by a second parting.

By half-past five on the clock all was ready. The ladies had had a hurried meal, and were now lingering in the Queen's chamber, putting on their hoods and redingotes, while their serving-women gathered together their night attire and various other odds and ends, and packed them in one of the two coffers that still remained open on the floor. Very slowly they closed it, and began to cord it up. Any close observer, watching their leisurely movements, might have suspected that they were waiting for something, and working slowly to gain time. Suddenly one of the ladies, Lady Janet Douglas, who had been standing with her ear close to the door which separated the Queen's apartment from that of the young King, turned round sharply. " Master Kincaid, the tutor, hath gone," she said. " I heard the outer door close behind him, and his Majesty gave that little rap on the wall that he promised to give." The manner of everyone in the room changed in an instant. It was plain that the plot had been well discussed and everyone knew exactly what to do.

" Quick, Janet ! The dummy !" whispered the

Queen, throwing back the bedclothes of her bed, and lifting a pillow shaped and dressed to represent a child, she thrust it into Janet Douglas's arms. That lady vanished into the next room with her burden, and reappeared in a moment with the little King, whom she helped hurriedly into his clothes. " Mercifully it is black darkness in there," she said, " and owing to your Highness's orders they are not likely to draw back the curtains for another two hours or more."

Meanwhile two of the other ladies, Katherine Seton and Isabel Fletcher, had completed their outdoor attire ·and hurried out to the courtyard in readiness to engage the Chancellor and tutor in conversation should they chance to be waiting there. There was no loitering now in the chamber. Everyone was in feverish haste to be gone. Quickly the waiting-maids fastened up the coffers, in the second of which lay the little King, packed as carefully as though he had been made of crystal, among soft white coverings and fleecy shawls.

Then, as if from nowhere, appeared two of her Majesty's own bodyguard, who, if the truth must be told, had been hidden behind the arras. They carried out the boxes, and strapped them with infinite care on a waiting sumpter mule. " They had better make a start with the baggage, my Lord," suggested the Queen to the Chancellor, who was waiting in the courtyard, when this had been safely accomplished. "The mules are but slow, and we on our palfreys will quickly overtake them, for early though it be, there is none too much time. Also I have no wish that that poor bairn should wake, and have all the pain of parting over again."

"There is no fear of that," answered the Chancellor, who to tell the truth was feeling very regretful himself at the departure of his charming visitors. "He is a sound sleeper—and as you know, I have given strict orders that he be not disturbed. Ho there ! set on with the mules," he added, giving a nod to the captain in charge, and the little string of animals, with their burdens of boxes and bundles, swung out of the courtyard and began the rather steep descent to the Inner and Outer Barriers, and thence to the Castle Hill.

The Chancellor could not have spent more than ten minutes in his rather wordy farewells, but to the anxious Queen it seemed double that time, yet she dared not appear hurried, but listened patiently to his courteous assurances of the pleasure which her visit had given him, and his regrets that it had been so short. But at length it was all over. The last compliment had been paid, every farewell said, and the Queen and her retinue were at liberty to mount their palfreys and hasten after their precious baggage. They caught it up ere they had crossed the Castle Hill, and we may be sure that Queen Jane rode very close to the mule that carried a certain coffer, in case it should be knocked or jarred in any way on the short but anxious journey.

Seven o'clock passed, eight o'clock passed, nine o'clock passed, and up in the Castle there was no sign of the King. "Tell Master Kincaid to go in and wake the bairn," said the Chancellor when at last he discovered this fact. "We cannot let him sleep all day, and by giving him an extra two hours in his bed we have done all his mother could expect us to do. If he greets at her absence he greets, and that is the end of the matter."

But it was he himself, the Chancellor of Scotland, who was like to greet when Master Thomas Kincaid came rushing out of the King's apartment, his eyes staring, and a bunched-up pillow, with a scarlet nightcap, like what his Majesty wore, tied round the top of it, in his arms.

"He's gone," he cried wildly, "he's gone. And this thing"—and he shook the pillow in Sir William's face—"is left in his stead." It was only too true. The King *was* gone, and he, Sir William, had been fooled by a woman.

Messengers were dispatched in haste to Leith, while others were sent galloping to Dunbar to

cheery man, and loved full well the sound of horn
and hound, and when he kept court in Edinburgh
Castle he loved to hunt with his nobles in the
stretch of dark and dense forest-land that covered
the Pentland Hills. While engaged in this sport,
the Royal hunter time and again raised a snow-white
hind, which was so fleet of foot that it easily out-
distanced the swiftest hound, and always disappeared in the forest before the eyes of the chagrined
and disappointed King.

One day, when he had ridden to the great Castle
of Rosslyn, situated on the outskirts of the forest
some ten miles from Edinburgh, and had, with
his followers, been feasted there by Sir William
Saintclair, he spoke of the swift-footed hind which,
as he said, seemed to lead a charmed life, and
asked the nobles gathered round him, many of
whom lived in the neighbourhood, if there were no
hounds in their possession which could overtake
the animal.

The nobles looked at one another. Faith ! but
it's ill work entering into rivalry with the King, even
if 'tis only in the matter of hounds," they muttered,
and none of them would admit that his dogs could
rival those of the monarch.

But their host, Sir William, was a man of another
mould.

" By my troth, Sire," he said bluntly, " I have

here two hounds, Help and Hold, the like of which will not be found in the whole of broad Scotland. I will offer my head as a wager that, given an even start, the twain will pull down the hind ere she cross the burn that separates my estate of Rosslyn from thine of Pentland Moor."

The Bruce was somewhat nettled at this assurance that the Royal hounds could be so easily out-stripped.

"I accept the wager, Sir William," he cried, "and in good sooth I will hold thee to it. But as the head of a Scottish nobleman is too valuable to be risked for nothing, I will pit against it the whole of the Pentland Forest which stretches before us."

"Ho there!" he cried, turning to his huntsmen, chain up all the hounds save two ranches* with which to raise the quarry. Then let my Lord of Rosslyn unleash his dogs, and try whether he will lose his head or gain the Forest of Pentland."

Sir William gave an order to one of the huntsmen, who ran round the end of the Castle, and quickly reappeared with two great hounds in a leash by his side. No wonder their master had boasted of what they could do. They were great tawny brutes, with bloodshot eyes and hanging jowls. They stood higher than any hound belonging to the King or any of his nobles.

* Sleuth-hounds.

" It fears me that I have lost my forest," muttered
the monarch. " Who would have thought that
Saintclair would possess hounds like those ? They
were not bred in these parts, I trow."

" No, Sire; their mother came from France,
brought hither by a cousin of my Lord's," replied
a huntsman, " and for keenness of scent and swift-
ness of foot, they have few rivals."

By this time the party was in the depths of the
forest, and the ranches were nosing to and fro in
the thick underwood. Presently they gave voice
as if they had found their prey, and, with a crash
of brushwood, a great white hind bounded for one
moment into the open, and then disappeared among
the trees on the other side of the glade.

As she passed Sir William, who had reined in his
horse near by the King, she turned her head and
darted a glance at him, and to his wonder it seemed
as if the glance conveyed a sense of pained and
sad reproof.

Quick as thought, the huntsman let loose his pair
of hounds, and with two low, deep bays that sounded
like rumbling thunder, they darted into the wood
in pursuit, and were lost to sight. The horsemen
followed, and, after galloping for some time, they
emerged on the edge of an open space of greensward
on the other side of which flowed the March burn.

" Now may the Saints aid me," muttered the

3

Knight under his breath, " else is my head forfeit.
St. Catherine, my patroness, succour me ! If thou
wilt, I will build a chapel to the honour of thy
name."

In good sooth, it seemed as if his patroness had
heard him, for at that moment Help and Hold
seemed to quicken their pace, and gain rapidly on
the hind. The Earl, thinking, as was natural, only
of his head, galloped after them, urging them on
with shouts of encouragement ; but, even with all
their speed, it seemed as if the snow-white deer
would reach the burn before them.

She did ! plunging with one long leap into the
nut-brown water, for it had been a wet season, and
the burns were in spate.

But just as the horrified spectators drew up their
horses, aghast at the fate which Earl William's
rash wager had brought upon him, she stopped in
her course, hesitated, and finally stood still in the
middle of the stream, thus allowing the two great
hounds to come up to her.

With fierce yelps of triumph they threw themselves upon her, burying their fangs in her throat,
and when from loss of blood she staggered down
on her knees, they dragged her with ferocious
cruelty to the side of the burn. She fell at Earl
William's feet, and looked up at him with such a
world of pathetic reproach in her eyes, that never,

till he fell fighting the Moors in Spain,* did the
sight fade from his memory.

When it was seen that Help and Hold had
justified their master in making the wager, all his
fellow-nobles crowded round Saintclair, congratu-
lating him because his head was still on his shoulders,
and because he had added many broad acres to his
inheritance. Even the King himself, shaking off
his chagrin, rode forward frankly and held out his
hand.

"You have won the day, Sir William," he said,
"by the help of your buirdly hounds. And well
you deserve it, for. I have not witnessed a chase
like that for many a long year. Gladly do I cede
thee the Forest of Pentland, and appoint thee
Master of Venery therein. With Help and Hold
as your assistants, I trow the country folk will no
longer complain of the damage to their crops, for
the wild deer will have little rest."

But tho' he thanked the monarch on bended knee,
and acknowledged the good wishes of his friends,
Sir William's face was grave and clouded as he rode
back to the Castle, and, as his fellow-nobles returned
to Edinburgh in the train of the King, they said
wonderingly to one another that he looked more

---

* Sir William was one of the three noblemen chosen to
carry the heart of Bruce to Jerusalem. On the way he was
killed in Spain.

like a man who had lost an estate than one who had found one.

And could they have seen the master of Rosslyn at that moment, they would have been confirmed in their opinion.

For when he had ridden into the courtyard of his Castle, he had flung his horse's reins to his attendant, and, spurning the fawning hounds that would have flung themselves upon him in delight, he strode up to his own little chamber in the turret where his armour was kept. Bolting the door, he flung himself on a settle, and remained there without moving till it grew dusk, staring out over the wooded ravine on the brink of which the Castle stands.

In vain his gentle wife knocked at the door and craved for entrance. A black mood was upon him, and he would fain be left alone. For he felt in his spirit that the death of the noble white hind had boded some ill to him and his family.

" She looked on me so pitifully, and yet with such reproach in her eyes," he muttered to himself, " as if in some wise she gave her life for mine. As in good sooth she did. And yet methought she upbraided me for ever entering on the chase and bringing it to such an end. I wish I had not spoken with bragging lips to the King, then would Help and Hold have remained in their kennels, and this strange, stately creature be safe in her lair."

When night fell, he withdrew to his couch, but sleep refused to come to him, and he tossed from side to side in fevered unrest. Towards morning he fell into an uneasy doze, and, whether in vision or dream I know not, he saw, enacted again before his eyes, the discovery and pursuit of the white hind. This time he knew clearly, as clearly as if someone had declared it to him, that her death would bring sorrow and disaster to his house. And yet she had to die, for she lay there as if bound hand and foot, powerless to prevent it.

After the dogs had accomplished their deadly work, and she lay stretched on the green sward, a whisper seemed to come to him from some invisible presence :

" O day of infinite woe to thee and thine ! For thou hast slain the guardian of the brightest jewel that adorns thy House. From henceforth thy life will be dark and thy heart desolate."

Wide awake now, Sir William leaped from his bed and rushed into the open air. What was meant by the jewel of his House ? He asked the question of himself as he paced up and down, glancing at the dense masses of cloud which were piling up in the west, obscuring the moon, and giving promise of a storm.

The answer came unbidden to his mind. For dearly as he loved his gentle wife, the Lady Isabel, and near to his heart as was his infant son, there was one who was nearer and dearer still, his blue-eyed, golden-haired daughter Rosabelle, who was the very apple of his eye.

But what danger could threaten her? How could she be affected in any way by the death of the snow-white hind? Was she not thirty miles away, safe in Fife with her aunt, his sister, who, a couple of months ago, had come on a visit to Rosslyn, and had taken the joyous-hearted maiden back with her to stay for a few weeks at her Castle of Ravensheuch, in the fertile kingdom of Fife.

Rosabelle had her trustworthy waiting-woman with her, who had been her foster-mother in her infancy, and who would gladly lay down her life for that of her young mistress, and a score of men-at-arms, vowed to guard her day and night.

"Nay," muttered Sir William to himself with a grim smile, "my little Rosabelle is in good sooth my fairest jewel; but she hath better and stronger guardians than a forest hind, no matter how stately and uncommon the beast appeared. Methinks I am bewitched to let my rest be broken by a silly midnight dream."

He turned to retrace his steps to the Castle, and as he did so his limbs stiffened, and his face grew white and drawn. He looked like a man that had seen a ghost, but it was no ghost that confronted him. It was a wonderful and majestic sight, yet a sight that carried its own fell portent.

For close to the Castle stood the old church of St. Matthew, where the Lords of the House of Rosslyn were christened and wed and buried, not in coffins of wood like other men, but shrouded in their coats of mail.

And tonight this ancient church was an awesome sight, for, like the burning bush spoken of in the Good Book, it was burning with fire, and yet it was not consumed. Every pinnacle and buttress, every stone and pillar stood out red as blood in the fierce blaze of flame. Through the traceried windows, Sir William could see the interior of the church: the Altar, the richly carved pillars, the images of Saints and Angels all aglow in the unearthly light.

It was an awesome and yet beautiful spectacle, but at the sight of it the heart of Saintclair felt heavy as lead, and he uttered a sorrowful groan. For he knew too well the legend of his House, that on the eve of the death of one of its members the ancient church at midnight appeared to be in flames.

" Not Rosabelle, not Rosabelle !" he cried, throwing up his hands entreatingly to the storm-tossed sky, for already the wind had risen and the tempest was breaking.

But the fiery-tinted clouds gave back no answer, and the distracted father had perforce to shelter from the storm by going back to his chamber and pacing backwards and forwards, awaiting the dawn and the dire tidings which he felt certain the new day would bring.

Nor was he mistaken in his fears. The portent of Rosslyn proved only too true.

For hours a terrible storm, such as had not been known to living man, raged over the district, both on land and sea.

And in the morning, when it had passed and the wind fell, planks and spars, and poor broken bodies of those who but yesterday had been hardy seamen, were cast up on the shore. They were Saintclair's men, those who had manned the boat which had carried the daughter of the House over the shining Forth, which now sparkled so peacefully under the morning sky. They had been bringing her back, apparently, when the storm broke and disaster befell.

A maiden's whim had caused the tragedy. At least, so it was ever said, and Sir William never denied it. The Lady Rosabelle and the young Lord Lindesay had been youth and maiden together. No troth had been plighted—no vows taken. Yet where one went the other followed, and those who watched them whispered to each other: " Saw ye ever such a gallant pair ?"

Young Lindesay rode in the Bruce's train, and, Rosabelle, far away in Fife, yearned to be at home to see her lover ride by in all his festal array. So, heedless of her aunt's entreaties or the signs of the coming storm, she had ordered the sailors to man the boat, and had set out in haste on her homeward voyage. And the storm had broken, and calamity had come, and the brightest jewel of the House of Rosslyn had perished in the sea.

It was all true, in its measure. These things had happened, and had led to the appointed end; but if the King had not given the challenge, and Sir William had not accepted it, if the hounds had not left their kennel, and the snow-white hind had not been killed, who can say that fair Rosabelle might not have come safe to land?

These were the questions which, through the darkened years that remained to him, her father asked himself reproachfully, and to which he could find no answer.

III

A KNIGHT OF THE CROSS

THERE was running to and fro in the ancient Tower of Kilchurn, which stands on a rocky promontory at the east end of Loch Awe.

For the Lord of the Castle, Sir Colin Campbell, had heard the cry of the Crusaders, " God wills it " ; and, his heart answering to the call, he had put his affairs in order, handed over the management of his estate to his young wife, the Lady Jacquetta, and was now on the point of riding away to join the King of England, Richard the Lion-hearted, and fare with him to the Holy Land, there to fight the infidel and rescue the Holy Places out of pagan hands.

" Fare thee well, sweetheart," he said, as, clad in full armour, he came down into the courtyard of his little tower, and stooped to kiss his wife and infant son, ere he mounted his waiting steed. " My lands and my honour I leave in thy keeping. Do thy best for the former for our son's sake, as well as for mine. As for the latter, I know full well it is more dear to thee than aught on earth. By God's mercy I shall return again, if so it be His will. But if I

fall, I fall under His Banner, therefore thou wilt
have His special protection and that of His Blessed
Saints."

Then the gallant-hearted man rode off, and his
wife was left to rule the Castle in his stead, and
gather in the rents, and see to the management of
the estate and the well-being of her husband's
clansmen. She was quite equal to the task, however,
for she was strong-minded and vigorous, even though
she was little more than a girl, and her whole heart
was set on fulfilling her dear Lord's command and
carrying out his wishes.

Now there was one thing that had ever been near
Sir Colin's heart, and he had often spoken to her
about it.

This was, that some day, when he had gathered
enough money he should enlarge his little Tower,
and make it more like the Castles that other chieftains had.

" I should like my son, when he rules in my stead,
to have a Castle that is worth its name, not merely
an old keep formed of four plain walls."

Jacquetta remembered how often she had heard
him say this, and slowly the resolve formed in her
mind that she would build a fair and goodly Castle
to greet the eyes of her Lord on his return.

So she lived very, very plainly in her little old
Tower, keeping no waiting-maid for herself, only

a nurse for the child, and doing without many things that other women of her rank considered necessary. And as the rents came in, she laid them aside, grudging every penny she had to take for her own use, until she had saved quite a goodly sum. Then she sent for masons and builders, and consulted with them over plans, and set them to work, and by-and-by the walls of a magnificent Castle rose round the little Tower. For she knew that her husband would want his old roof-tree to be the heart and centre of his new home.

Years passed away, and while the Lady Jacquetta was living her simple life at home, and using the money which she might have spent on herself in completing the fair dwelling which she was preparing for her husband, Sir Colin had fought many a deadly fight with the Saracens, and had taken his part right nobly in delivering the Holy Sepulchre out of their hands and giving it into Christian keeping.

An old chronicler has left it on record that "through valiant actes and manhood, he was made Knight in the Isle of Rhodes," a title which he ever afterwards bore.

As if protected by his dear wife's prayers, no hurt had befallen him, and his heart was at rest; for he had taken care, when he could, to find out some disabled soldier, who, no longer able to fight, was returning home. Then, giving the man a packet of letters and a present of gold, he made him promise to travel to Kilchurn and deliver the packet to the Lady of the Castle, and tell her of his, Sir Colin's, welfare.

But at the end of seven years it chanced that one night as Sir Colin, now a great commander in the crusading army, lay asleep in his tent in the desert, he had a strange and frightening dream.

He dreamt that a monk appeared to him clad in the white habit of the monks of Ardchattan, a Priory which stood not many miles from Kilchurn.

"Arise and gird thyself, thou Knight of the Cross," said the strange visitant, "and set off on thy journey homewards at once, for a deadly evil threatens thy House. If thou canst reach Loch Awe in time, it may be averted, but there is need of haste. Lo! I have warned thee, and I do not speak with a light or careless tongue." The monk vanished, and Sir Colin awoke, bathed in perspiration and trembling in every limb.

"'Tis a far cry to Loch Awe," he muttered, "but by Our Lady's help I will be there in time, or leave my bones for the craws to pick on the road."

Without a moment's delay he rose and dressed himself, and, without waking even his body-servant, made his way to the General's tent. Next morning, when the bugles blew for the reveille, Sir Colin Campbell was gone, no man knew whither.

Some weeks later old Sheilagh Cameron was hanging out her washing on the straggling thorn hedge that surrounded the little bit of ground where she grew her scanty supply of potherbs and simples. She had been nurse at the Tower of Kilchurn when the present Lord was a child, and in reward for her faithful services he had given her her little cottage in the clachan of Succoth, where she had been born, which stood about a mile from the Castle on the Loch.

She had not noticed a dusty and footsore wayfarer approaching, until he stopped on the other side of the hedge and spoke to her. Then she saw that he was a palmer, for he carried a pilgrim's staff, and a little cross of palms was fastened on his broad-brimmed hat.

" Good-day, Grannie, and how goes it all in this countryside ?" he asked. And though his face was strange to her, being as brown as a berry, and almost covered by a huge black beard, there was something about his voice that sounded curiously familiar to Sheilagh's ear.

" Things go well enough, goodman," answered the old woman, peering with her sharp little eyes at the traveller's face. " Tho' none of us like the notion of a new master at the Castle. One would think our Lady deserved a better fate than to wed the black McCorquodale, after all she hath done, pinching and scraping in order that she might gather money enow to build a fair new Castle against her Lord's home-coming. And as the walls have gone up she hath wellnigh broken her heart looking for the news from the East that hath never come. No ! not a word, though my Lord hath been gone these seven years and more. And that sour-faced McCorquodale, whom none of us would trust further than we could see him, hath threeped and threeped down her throat that my Lord is dead, he that was the bonnie bairn that I nursed at my ain breast. And at last he hath persuaded her that the thing is true. He was away across the Border lately—or so he said—and when he came back he brought tidings, which he pretended he had got from one who hath returned from the East, that my Lord is indeed dead, having been killed at a place they call Acre. Moreover, he hath threatened to take all the lands of Kilchurn if my Lady will not wed him, and the poor thing is so bewildered with sorrow and disappointment that she hath given in, and the marriage will take place tomorrow."

" Now, by St. Michael and all the Saints, that shall it not," cried the palmer, flinging one arm in the air with an angry gesture. As he did so, his tattered sleeve fell back, revealing a sinewy arm, with a deeply marked scar across it.

At the sight old Sheilagh dropped her basket of

clothes and threw up her hands to the blue sky.

"To think I didna' ken my bairn," she exclaimed, "till I saw the scar he got when he fell against the reaper's sickle, that summer's day so long gone by. By all that is holy, Sire, where have ye come from, and where have ye been, that ye have sent no message, and wellnigh let a black cuckoo enter your nest?"

"I have been where it was my duty to be, Sheilagh," answered Sir Colin gravely; "but no man can say I sent no word. For every year I have sent a message with some trusty messenger, to say that I was alive and unharmed."

"Well, the trusty messengers have never got the length o' Kilchurn," said Sheilagh, "tho' whether they got the length o' McCorquodale's or no, I wouldna' venture to say. His house stands on the road by which they must pass. He's false enough and sly enough to set a watch for any stranger that might bear the badge of the Crusades, and either wrest the message from him or do away with him altogether. Be that as it may, I can give ye my oath that your Lady hath never heard one word from ye since ye rode away seven long years ago. Leal and true hath she been, and muckle fash hath she taken to prepare a wonderful surprise and welcome for ye, against the time ye should return. But aye hath she been threatened and hindered by this false man McCorquodale, who hath pretended to be a friend when all the time he hath been coveting her lands and planning her downfall. And of late the poor lassie's heart hath grown heavy, and the hope of thy return hath died, and she hath yielded to his importunity, just because her spirit is wellnigh broken."

" But she is not wedded yet ? " cried Sir Colin, for in good troth it was he.

" No, by Our Lady's grace, that catastrophe hath been avoided. But thou art come only in the nick of time. For tomorrow was the wedding Mass to be said down in the little chapel in the glen. And at this very moment, if I mistake not, a great feast is being held at the Castle, as would be but fitting and right, were it not that the heart of the Lady who gives it is as heavy and cold as that bit o' lead yonder."

Without another word Sir Colin seized his pilgrim's staff, and took his way in haste up the hill, on the other side of which lay Loch Awe and his ancestral home. When he reached the top he stopped, breathless with astonishment. For there, far below him, lay the peaceful Loch, just as he had known it from his boyhood's days. But his own Keep Tower ! That had changed completely. Or rather, it still stood there, but only as part of

4

a magnificent Castle, with pepperpot turrets and crowstepped gables, which might compare favourably with the Castle of MacCallum More himself!

So that was what old Sheilagh had meant when she spoke of her young mistress slaving and stinting herself to provide a surprise for him against his return! And that false traitor, McCorquodale, who had doubtless trapped his messengers, was expecting Castle, lands, and Lady to fall into his hands.

" Now, by St. Bryde of Kilmun, he'll have to face the reckoning," muttered Sir Colin, as he plunged down the hillside waist-deep in bracken. Ten minutes later he was standing before the door of his grand new Castle, and he gave a knock on it with his staff, which resounded like thunder throughout the building.

" May Our Lady shield us! but who may that be who knocks so furiously?" exclaimed the porter, as he put down the tasty morsel of roasted moorfowl which he was eating, and hurried along the vaulted passage to open the door.

He expected to find at least a knight in armour, and a frown gathered on his face when he saw no one but a poor palmer, who, to judge from his staff and cross of palms, had been on pilgrimage to the Holy Land.

" Certes! but whatever else thou hast learned on

thy travels, fellow, thou hast not learned the grace
of humility, else wouldst thou not attempt to
batter down the Castle. Dost thou think we have
all lost our hearing?" he asked angrily.

"I took for granted everyone was busy at the
table," said the palmer calmly. "So I knocked
loudly to gain attention."

The porter stared. He was not accustomed to
be spoken to like this, but there was something in
the bearing of the stranger which prevented him
answering back as he would like to do. Besides, the
man was plainly a pilgrim, and as such was entitled
to what hospitality the Castle could afford.

"What wilt thou, then, holy man?" he asked,
speaking as sullenly as he dared.

"Merely bite and sup," replied the Palmer, "but
the latter must I have from the hands of the mistress
of the house, else will a curse fall on the wedding
which I hear takes place tomorrow."

Once more the porter stared. He felt he could
not ask the Lady Jacquetta to come down from the
great hall, where she sat, like a queen, at the head
of the table, to serve this beggar man in the dusty
tattered clothes. But he was a palmer, and as such
might possess unknown powers, and might bless
or curse as he felt inclined! So he thought it would
be best to humour him, and seem as if he were
going to obey his behest.

Bidding the unwelcome guest come into the hall and rest himself on the great oak settle in the embrasure by the window, the porter hastened to the kitchen and brought back a tray, laden with an ample supply of roasted meat and a loaf of fine white bread. There was also a goblet of red wine, but this the palmer put aside.

" I tell thee I can only drink from a goblet given to me by thy Lady herself. Go and whisper to her that a pilgrim from the East craves the boon. Go, fellow ! I tell thee more depends on thine obedience than thou knowest."

Puzzled by the stranger's insistence, the porter obeyed. Entering the hall unobserved he seized a platter from the side-table, and handed it on bended knee to his mistress, as he saw the other serving-men do. Greatly astonished, she was about to check him for his forwardness, but in a low voice he whispered the palmer's message. No sooner did she hear it than she sprang to her feet, and filled her own silver goblet with rich Malvoisie.

" Bring the pilgrim hither, and set a place for him here beside me. No man who hath been in the East, and who hath fought under the Holy Rood as my dear Lord fought, shall eat his food downstairs at the door, as if he were a common beggar."

McCorquodale, who was sitting beside her, heard what she said to the servant, and his dark face flushed whether with fear or anger, who can say?

"Heard ye ever the like?" he exclaimed, trying to push the Lady of the Castle back into her chair. "To ask a poor gangrel body to take his place at this fair board! Fill up your glass if ye will, madam, and send it down to him with your greeting. But let that suffice. He is no more likely to be a palmer than I am. Doubtless he hath borrowed both his staff and his palm-leaves, in order to open tender hearts like thine."

But the Lady Jacquetta turned to him with such a flash in her eyes that, rough and headstrong man as he was, he shrank back in his chair.

"I'll trouble you to mind your own business, John McCorquodale," she said, "and to remember, for this night at least, I am mistress here. The palmer may bring the long-looked-for message from my own true Lord. And whether he does so or no, it behoves us to succour him."

Then, turning to the servant, she added, "Haste thee, sirrah, and fetch him hither."

So the tattered and travel-stained pilgrim was brought up into the great hall, and a strange hush fell over the company as he strode up to where the Lady Jacquetta was seated, and, kneeling beside her, humbly kissed her robe.

"Welcome, Sir Palmer," she said, handing him

the goblet of wine that he might quench his thirst, and gazing wistfully at him as she did so. " They tell me that thou hast been in the East. Perchance thou art come to bring me a message from one whom I have long mourned as dead ?"

" Troth have I," replied the stranger, and at the sound of his voice many of the old family retainers who were seated round the table started. " I bring thee more than a message, I bring thee my own leal and loyal heart, and a thousand thanks for all that thou hast done for me. And here do I drink to the health of our House and the downfall of all false friends."

So saying, he sprang to his feet, and, raising the goblet in his right hand, drank its contents at one great gulp. As he did so, the sleeve of his tattered gown fell back, revealing the scar on his arm.

" Colin, my Colin !" cried Lady Jacquetta, in a voice shrill with rapture and surprise, and she threw herself into his arms.

" 'Tis Sir Colin, 'tis his Lordship himself," echoed the clansmen, leaving their seats and crowding round their Chief. Then ensued such a babel of voices, of tears and laughter, of questions and answers, that anyone who had entered at that moment would have thought that everyone had gone mad.

But there was one man who never spoke. And

that was John McCorquodale. With a furtive glance at the happy company, who were too busy and occupied to notice him, he stole from the room, and down the stair, and out through the open door into the darkness.

" Let him go," said Sir Colin, when at last his absence was observed, " and leave him alone with his conscience. Doubtless it will give him enough to think of. For that he stopped my messengers is certain, and I sore misdoubt me that the guilt of their blood rests on him. Be that as it may, I leave him to vengeance from Higher Hands. I will not mar the joy of my home-coming by any violent deed."

Sir Colin Campbell and his wife Jacquetta lived for many a long year in the new Castle of Kilchurn, and a family of gallant sons and fair daughters grew up round them. And as long as Sir Colin lived, John McCorquodale was safe, in spite of the wicked trick he had tried to play. But when that nobleman died, and his son reigned in his stead, the latter, not having fought under the Cross, and being of a rougher nature than his father, slew McCorquodale in fair fight, for the shame and dishonour which he had tried to bring upon the Lady Jacquetta, the mother whom he so dearly loved.

IV

OMERON CAMERON

" But how does it come that we possess land here in Braemar, Granny, land that is our own, and not held by rent or vassalage ? We are Camerons, and the Chief of our Clan has his Castle in the west, while here everyone bears the name of Mar, and, were a dispute to arise, would flock to the standard of the good Earl who lives up at Kildrummy Castle. Why, my father fell fighting for his Lordship's father, yet the Earl was a Mar, and my father was a Cameron. I just cannot understand it. " I have never troubled my head about it before ; I was born here and so was my father, and it seemed right that we should always be on the side of the Earl. But I was up on the hill this morning with red-headed Duncan and Black Rory, helping them to track the red-deer ; and Rory, who has been away up the glens, told Duncan that word had come that there was trouble brewing between the Campbells and the Camerons; and they both looked at me and laughed, and said it was time I was away over the mountains, to fight with my ain folk."

The speaker was a tall, well-made boy of twelve

or thirteen summers, clad in rough, home-made
leather garments, who stood leaning against the
lintel of the doorway of a small heather-thatched
house, which was nevertheless somewhat superior
as a dwelling to the low huts or hovels which formed
the little hamlet that lay under the walls of Kildrummy Castle, a quarter of a mile distant.

He was speaking to his granny, old Mirran
Cameron, who stood within by the very primitive
fireplace, stirring the contents of a three-legged
pot, which was hung over the fire by a chain and
swivel. She was dyeing sheep's wool black by
boiling it along with the roots of the white iris.
When this process was completed, she intended to
card and spin the wool into yarn, which would be
woven into a rough homespun cloth by Hamish
Mar down in the clachan, who had been to Edinburgh in his Lordship's train, and had there
mastered the intricacies of a rude hand-loom.

" Duncan and Black Rory would just be jealous
of thee, Donald, remembering that thou art a laird
in a small way, while they are but vassals, holding
their crofts by right of service. Not but thou
wouldst follow thy Lord, by whom I mean the Earl
of Mar, as gladly and readily as either red-headed
Duncan or Black Rory, but thou wouldst go of
thine own will as a laird—they would be bound to
go, as my Lord's clansmen."

Donald, boy as he was, had the sense to smile at the old woman's proudly spoken words, and his eyes wandered over the tiny strip of land which was all he could call his own; but he did not wish to vex her, for she had been both father and mother to him ever since his parents had died—his father on the field of battle, his mother at his birth three months later.

"Well, never heed Duncan and Rory, Granny; tell me the story, for I know there is one. See, I will shut the door, and bring over two creepies, one for thee and one for me. I can stir thy wool as well sitting as standing, and we will be snug and warm in the low of the fire, and thou shalt tell me thy story."

He placed the two creepies one on each side of the fireplace as he spoke, throwing some pieces of peat on the embers, and he took the wooden spoon from the old woman's hand, and commenced to stir the ugly coloured mass in the pot, while his granny, with a sigh of relief, for she was near eighty and stiff with " the pains," rested her elbows on her knees and her face on her hands, and, staring dreamily into the glowing fire, began her story.

" 'Tis nigh sixty years ago, and your grandfather and me were young folk with two little bairnies to bring up, and little to do it with. Your grandfather was one of Cameron of Lochiel's men, and helped to gather the red-deer on the hills when his Lordship had a fancy for the chase. But our little hut was far up in a hidden glen, and for half the year we were wellnigh forgotten, no man caring overmuch whether we lived or died.

" We had a hard struggle, Omeron and me, to make ends meet, and to get food for ourselves and the two little ones, and clothing to keep us warm. Your grandfather had a wheen sheep and a little patch of corn, and it was a great day when we managed to scrape together enough siller to buy us a cow. And, as was natural, in due time the cow brought us a nice little brown calf. Take it on the whole, it was a hard life, harder than ever thou hast known it, Donald ; but we had good times and bad times, like other folk.

" At the time I am telling you about it was a bad time, with hardly a gleam of light to lighten it. It had been a cold, wet summer, and a wetter backend, so the corn, which had never fairly ripened, was blackened in the stooks ; so even the oatmeal for our porridge, which was what we mostly lived on, had a nasty mousened taste. Then some ailment had broken out among the sheep, and although we had plenty of braxy* to eat, there were only two left to carry on the flock in the spring. The very hens had left off laying with the wet, and had begun

* Braxy, the flesh of sheep which have died, not been killed.

to moult, and now sat up below the thatch with
hardly a feather to cover their bones.

" Things were very unsettled among the clansmen
also, though we were so cut off from the outside
world that we did not hear all that was going on.
But this we did know, that the King, who was
James, the first of his name, he who had spent his
youth as a prisoner in the King's braw palace in
England, had made up his mind, on his return to
his ain land, to do away with the raiding and law-
lessness which was all too common in this realm,
especially in the north. To this end he had sent
his lowland soldiers to join such chieftains as were
law-abiding and saw eye to eye with him in this
matter, and the combined forces worked together
to put down thieving and cruelty and to establish
some sort of law and order.

" They were succeeding fairly well, and that
summer it had been said that, in Lochaber at least,
the roads were safer than they had ever been, and
that women and bairns could live more securely
than they had been able to do in their lives before."

" But this state of things did not please the proud
and lofty Lords of the Isles, who looked on themselves as kings in their own domains, and were
feared that if the folk on the mainland submitted to
the King's laws, they in their turn would have to
do the same. So in order to frighten the folk on

the mainland, they left their islands, and came over to Lochaber, and wrought their cruel will there with fire and with sword. To check their wild advance, the heads of the northern clans, chief among them the Earl of Mar, our present Lordship's father, and his cousin, once removed, the Earl of Caithness, gathered their men together, and the last we had heard of them was, that they were gathered round Inverlochy Castle, on Loch Ness, there to make a stand and stem the progress of the Isles-men. Cameron of Lochiel took no hand in the matter, so we, his clansfolk, were not called on to rise.

"Well do I mind the cold November afternoon when snow began to fall just in the gloaming, and your grandfather, after bringing in some armfuls of peat, went away up the hill to the fir-wood to cut down a backful of thick fir branches, for it looked like being a feeding storm, and it behoved us to have plenty of fuel at hand. He brought down one backful, and went up for another, and by this time the snow lay two or three inches deep, and the wind was swirling it into drifts. I was a bit anxious till he reappeared, for I have known, more than once, a man to lose all sense of airt* in weather like that, and wander away and perish in the snow. So I was relieved when I heard him

* Direction.

push open the door, and I hurried to help him in with the fir-wood.

"But what was my astonishment to see that besides the wood on his back, he bore on his arm a half-swooning man. It was clear that the stranger was a soldier, and an officer of rank—his silver-mounted dirk and the richly chased hilt of the sword he wore told one that; but his plaid and his kilt were so matted and discoloured with earth and blood that one could scarce distinguish the colours of the tartan, so there was nothing to guide one as to what clan he belonged to.

"He had gotten a waesome clyte* on the head, for one side of his face was all black and swollen, and his right eye was clean out of sight. I could see that his hair was dark and thick with blood under his glengarry. He was fair spent with weakness and fatigue, and your grandfather had wellnigh to trail him over the threshold, yet his unhurt eye was wild and glittering, as if some fever were fastening upon him.

"'Steek and bar the door behind us,' said my husband, and as he spoke he lowered the stranger on to the heap of dry heather which, covered with a plaid, served the two bairns for a bed, and then got rid of his load of wood. 'He is a King's man, whoever he be,' he went on, looking down at the

* Blow.

unexpected visitor, 'for he is better clad than the Islesmen. They fight almost naked, like savages. But he is worn out and wellnigh famished. He staggered out of the wood and fell at my feet, as I was cutting down the last of my branches, and a bonny job I had to get him up and guide him down the hill. Another half-hour in this blizzard, and it would have been another soldier lost to the King's Majesty. It would have been a pity, for he's a braw and buirdly man.'

" 'What do you think can have happened?' I whispered, afraid of the stranger overhearing our remarks, tho' to be sure, he seemed to have sunk into unconsciousness.

" ' I canna tell you that,' answered my husband, ' for he was too far spent even to speak ; but I jalouse there maun have been a battle fought, and if this gentleman be a specimen of the survivors, I sair misdoubt me the King's army must hae lost the fight. But see, Elspeth, my lass, we canna stand clavering here, else will he die on our hands. Put on the pot, and get some hot water to wash his feet, for his brogues are torn to pieces, and the flesh is cut and blistered by the rocks and the roots of the heather. As for that wound on his head, cut away the hair and bathe it, and see if ye can find a bit of clean linen stuff to bind it up.'

" I looked round helplessly. As I have said, the

times were hard, and we were very poor, and a bit of linen, even tho' it were only a rag, was ill to come by.

" ' I have nothing of linen at all,' said I, ' save the long-tailed robe that her old Ladyship of Lochiel gave me when Alistair was born, and which he and his brother wore when they were carried down the glen to the chapel to be christened.'

" ' Then ye'll just have to take that,' replied Omeron, ' for a cut like this needs something clean and soft. I ken it goes against your heart to take it, my lass,' he added softly, ' but we canna help it. Do ye think we could kill a couple of these hens up in the thatch ? For the poor man stands much in need of strong soup and tender meat, if he is to be nursed back to health, and methinks there is naught else in the house but oatcakes and oatmeal.'

" ' Kill the hens !' I retorted, tears filling my eyes and a lump rising in my throat at this other demand on my scanty resources. The christening robe was one of my few treasures. I kept it, and a bit of my wedding frock, and the string of cairngorm stones which Omeron had picked up one by one in the burn, and had strung together and had given me on the day we promised to wed one another, all tied up in a bundle, which was hidden above the press in the corner, and which I had vowed I would never part with, no matter how poor we were.

" As for the hens, I depended on their eggs for meat for the bairns when they were out of sorts and milk was scarce—as it often was, especially in lambing time—and on their feathers (when they died, for I was never wasteful enough to *kill* a hen) to fill a little poke with, on which a child could lay its head when it had a pain there.

" ' Oh, Omeron,' I cried, ' I just canna' let ye kill a hen, we have so few. Besides they are in the middle of the moult, and are nothing but rickles of bones. I'll tear up the christening robe if it pleases you, but I just canna let ye take the hens.'

" ' Aweel, I'll just have to take something else,' said Omeron, ' for ye ken the Highland law of hospitality. We canna let a stranger die on our hands—and this one looks fairly like doing it— without trying to succour him with the best that we can offer.'

" His words made me feel rather ashamed, so without saying any more I made haste to get the water and attend to the wounded man, while Omeron went out into the storm, shutting the door behind him. By the time he came back I had the stranger more comfortable, with his feet washed clean, and anointed with some grease which I had gotten from a dead stag, and rinded down, and his wound bathed, and bound up with a strip of my much-thought-of bairn's robe.

" I was half sorry about the hen now, for the soldier was beginning to shiver, and I clearly saw that he needed something hot and strengthening; and, moreover, I had nothing to lay over him but his own dirty plaid, unless Omeron and me and the bairns were to sleep this bitter night bare of what poor wrappings we had for blankets. Not that the hen could have provided a covering, but hot soup would have put some heat in him and helped to keep out the cold.

" I little reckoned how near food and covering were, or whence they had been obtained. The door opened and Omeron came in, a smoking quarter of newly killed beef under one oxter, a dark red hide over the other. My very heart stood still ! He had killed the red calf, which by now had been almost a stirk ! Better, ten times better, half a dozen hens than this !

" 'Oh, Omeron !' I cried, 'how could you, and us with two bairns to feed ! In another year it would have been a quey, and maybe it would have had a calf.'

" ' Calf or no calf, I had to do it,' answered Omeron. ' A hen might have served one day or two, but it will be a month o' days before the stranger can travel, and we must have broth for him to sup as long as the fever is on him, and strong meat for him to eat after that. Forbye the skin

here will make a hap for him, he canna lie there
wrapped in nothing but his plaid. So put some of
this in the pot, we'll all be the better of a good hot
meal on this bitter night, and I'll salt the rest of the
meat when daylight comes in the morning. I have
hung it up in the byre.'

"It was true what Omeron said. We *were* the
better for a hot pot of broth, and a little colour
came into the stranger's cheeks when I got a spoon-
ful or two of it down his throat. He even opened
his eyes and looked at me as if there was a glimmer
of sense in his brain.

"Omeron brought an armful of dry heather, and
put it down by the side of the wall near the hearth,
and spread the stirk's skin on it, with the hairy
side up. Then he took the dirty, blood-stained
clothing from the wounded man, and, lifting him
in his arms, carried him over to the hastily prepared
bed, and covered him with his plaid, and then
happed the skin over him, so that he was as warm
and cosy as a bairn in its cradle.

"More than that, he sat up with him half the
night, giving him a drop of broth now and then, and
he would not come and lie down beside me till he
had seen him fall into a quiet, natural sleep. In
spite of his care, however, it was three or four days
before the gentleman's full consciousness came
back, tho' he had blinks of sense now and then, and

I would catch him watching me as I tidied the house, or patched the bairns' already well-patched clothes.

" He did not speak much, even when he was able first to sit up, then to walk about the hut. He was a grand listener, though, and so homely and simple that I found myself telling him all about Omeron and me and the bairns, and how hard it was to live, before ever I knew that I had begun to speak.

" The snow went on for six days after his arrival, then hard frost set in, so that the glens were blocked with solid wreaths of snow, which were so hard and firm that no one could cut a way through them. So we were left unmolested, and even our nameless visitor (for he never told us what they called him, and there was something about him which kept us from asking) seemed to feel quite safe from any pursuit.

" But when the weather changed and a fresh wind blew, which began to melt the snow as quickly as if you had poured hot water upon it, he grew uneasy, and used to start whenever a noise was heard outside, and as his strength came back it was plain to see he was in a hurry to be gone. He had never, up till now, gone outside the hut; but one fine sunny morning he asked Omeron if he would keep him company up to the top of the hill, and show him the track that led down into Braemar.

" ' I come from that countryside,' he said, ' and I will be safe enough when once I am over the mountains. I have been long enough here, and I would be sorry were trouble to fall on the two of you for my sake.' So after a hearty breakfast of oatcakes and salt beef, for the stirk had lasted well, Omeron and he set out. He shook me by the hand and thanked me most warmly before he left, for all the trouble I had taken over him, and said that he was vexed that it was not in his power to repay me at the moment, but that he hoped he might have a chance to do so in the future.

" I confess I paid but little heed to his words, for the Camerons have little comings and goings with the folk o' Braemar, and I never expected to see him again. And it fears me that, when he and Omeron had disappeared round the corner of the hill, my covetous heart went back to the thought of the spoilt christening robe and the dead stirk.

" But I sang a different song when Omeron came back late in the afternoon. I thought something by-ordinar had happened even before I saw him, by the sound of his step, which had more spring in it than usual, and by the way he burst open the door.

" ' Do you ken who the stranger is, Elspeth ?' he cried.

" ' No ; how could I, for he never told us ?' I

replied. ' An officer on the side of the King. So much we learned from his talk about the battle, but beyond that he told me nothing.'

" ' He is an officer in the King's army, sure enough,' said Omeron, ' but he is more. He is a belted Earl, the Earl o' Mar himself, and he made me promise that if any hurt comes to us for harbouring him, as well it may, for bands of the Islesmen are still lingering about, and there may be some damage done before the King's party rallies again, we have just to pack up our bits of things and go over the hill to his country, and he will see to it that we are provided for.'

" A belted Earl ! And I had washed him and tended him and fed him with as little ceremony as if he had been my own Neil or Alistair, for, at first, in his weakness, he had just seemed to me like one of them. If I had known, I would have slipped in a ' Sir,' and a ' my Lord,' and ' if it please thee ' when I was speaking to him, but it was no use regretting things like that now, and maybe he would overlook my want of manners for the service I had rendered him.

" He had spoken to Omeron about the risk of evil befalling us for having sheltered him, and his words came only too true. For when Omeron was up on the hillside one morning just ten days after he left, a party of men came to the door, clad in such wild-looking garments, fashioned for the most part of deerskin, that it did not need their outlandish speech to tell me that they came from the Isles. My heart leaped into my mouth at the sight of them, for I knew they came on no friendly errand. By signs as well as words they made me understand that they sought my goodman in order to punish him for sheltering my Lord of Mar, and they did not leave me in doubt of what fate awaited Omeron if he had the misfortune to fall into their hands. But Providence had a care for us, and kept him on the hills, while they turned and went down the glen by the road they came. But not before they had set a light to the hut, and burned it to the ground before our eyes.

"So when at last Omeron came back, it was to find his home gone, and his wife and bairns crouching, half distraught, in the byre, which, being hidden in a clump of trees, the Islesmen had by good luck overlooked. But your grandfather was aye a stout-hearted man, which was a mercy, for I was inclined to be fearsome and timorous, and he lifted little Neil on his back, and took Alistair by the hand. 'Now is the time to test my Lord of Mar's promise,' he said. 'Fill a poke with oatmeal, Elspeth—there is some in a barrel in the corner—and put a luggie in the mouth of it, and let loose the cow. We'll take the road over the hills, and we'll drive her in front of us. She'll give a drop of milk even when she is travelling, and with that and the meal we'll manage till we reach the Earl's Castle, Kildrummy, he calls it. 'Tis better that we get as far on our road as we can ere darkness falls, for fear some more of these Islesmen come up the glen, and we lose more than the hut and the hens.' For these poor creatures, who had still been moulting among the rafters, had perished in the flames.

" So, with little time for thought, I undid the cow, and, driving her in front of us, we began our toilsome journey up the steep mountainside, and over the wild and stony passes that led us by Cairn Toul and Ben Macdhui, to the more innerly valleys that we ken as the Braes o' Mar.

" We stayed that night in a cave on the hillside, but the two next we had to sleep in the open, huddled together for warmth, for with the bairns and the cow we travelled but slowly, and it was not until the afternoon of the fourth day that we arrived at the gate of Kildrummy Castle. You may not think so much of it, Donald, for you have grown up under its shadow, and you are accustomed to its size and importance; but to Omeron and me, worn and footsore as we were, and hungry into the bargain, the King's Castle in Edinburgh could not have looked grander.

" The sight of it made us feel very outlandish

I UNDID THE COW, AND WE BEGAN OUR TOILSOME JOURNEY

and poor as we went up to the big gateway, ever driving the cow in front of us, especially as we could see that the courtyard within the Castle wall was filled with gentry amusing themselves by some kind of tournament and games, whilst the ladies of the Castle, seated on a high raised platform at one end, watched them and cheered the victors.

" Round the open gateway were gathered the serving-men and other vassals, and, as you may think, every eye was turned on us as we went up the brae that leads to the entrance.

" But we went steadily on, for your grandfather was not a man to be easily daunted, and at last we were standing before the porter at the gate and telling our story. But to our bewilderment the man burst into a shout of laughter, which was echoed by those around him.

" ' A likely tale, thou villain!' he cried. ' Dost thou think my Lord is going to succour all the beggars who care to tramp the country with their bairns, and tell long stories about their houses being burned? If your house was burned, why was the cow not driven away? As for you being the man that sheltered my Lord, every Cameron in Lochiel may say the same thing. Na, na, I'll give you a bit of bread for the sake o' the bairns, an' then ye maun just be tramping, you and your cow, and think yourselves very lucky that we Mars are honest folk and dinna take her from you.'

" Again all the listeners laughed, and at the sound some of the gentry turned their heads in our direction to see what the sport was.   I was so tired and so shamed at the men's laughter, and also at the looks they cast on me, that I would fain have hung my head and slunk away, but Omeron was not to be downed, and once more raised his voice, and began to argue with the guard, declaring that what he said was true, and demanding to speak with the Earl o' Mar.

" ' Speak with his Lordship !   Did ye ever hear the like o' that?   Dost thou think the Earl is going to be troubled to come and speak to a vagabond like thee?   If thy story be true he must have given thee a note or a token of some sort.   If thou canst produce that, then I will listen to thy words.'

" But this poor Omeron could not do, for the Earl had only given him his word, and it seemed as if in truth we might be driven away; but, as good guiding would have it, at that moment Alistair, frightened by the unkind faces, began to greet, and Neil followed his example, and the more I tried to hush them, the louder they roared, till there was enough din to bring down the Castle walls.   Oh ! I was sore shamed and affronted, and could think of nothing but the wish that the ground beneath my feet would open up and swallow me.

" But it was the best thing that could have happened. For a little laddie who was sitting among the braw ladies on the platform rose and jumped down and came running out to see what the stir was about.

" It was the Earl's grandson, he who bears the title today. He stood and stared at the greeting bairns, and his bonnie face clouded over as he saw their tired looks and tattered clothes.

" ' Take this,' he said at last, pulling a little wooden poupet* out and thrusting it into Alistair's hand.

" The bairns had hardly ever had a toy in their lives, and this unexpected gift made them stop their noise as suddenly as they had begun, as they examined the rough-cut little mannikin, whose coat had been painted red and his kilt green.

" Omeron was still arguing with the guards, and the young gentleman must have heard something he said, for he suddenly turned and ran up to one of the gentry who was playing at the bowls, and tugged at his kilt until the player turned round and listened to what he said.

" When the laddie had finished, the gentleman threw down his ball and came striding across the courtyard with his head in the air and his sporran

* Doll.

swinging. When he came near us, I saw who it
was. The wounded stranger who had lain so long
on our bed of heather wrapped in the brown stirk's
skin !

"At his approach a hush fell on the group of
serving-men, who had been so rude and noisy only
a minute before, and even the porter who guarded
the gateway stood to attention and looked the least
bit frightened.

" ' Hello, fellow ! and what is this I hear? My
grandson tells me that thou art turning from my
gate the man whose wife saved my life. Thou didst
not know it was he, thou sayest ?' For the porter,
who looked humble enough now, had muttered
some excuse under his breath. ' Then thou shouldest
have carried his story to someone who could tell
thee ! Canst thou not tell an honest man when
thou seest one, even tho' his clothes be poor ?'

" Then he turned to Omeron and me, and shook
us warmly by the hand before all the serving-folk.

" Your grandfather, who aye had his wits about
him, fell on one knee and told him our tale—how
our hut had been burned by the Islesmen, with all
it contained, and nothing left us but the cow.

" ' So you brought her with you, as well as the
bairns,' said the Earl with a twinkle in his eyes, as
he looked at Crummie, who, heedless of Earl and
serving-men alike, had laid herself down on the

turf before the Castle gate, and was nibbling away at the sweet, short grass.

" I think he was pleased at our trust in his word, for he added : ' You did the right thing, and doubtless we'll find room for the cow as well as for yourselves.'

" Then he led us, just as we were, Omeron carrying Neil, and me leading Alistair, across the great courtyard where all the grand company had ceased their play to look at us, up to the platform, and he spoke to one of the ladies there, the best-looking of them all.

" ' Arbel,' he said, ' here are the man and his wife whom I told you of, who took me into their hut, when I was wellnigh spent, and nursed me back to life, and gave me of their best, when they had but little to spare. Aye, goodwife,' he went on, turning to me, ' I was often more sensible than you were aware of, and I knew all about the christening robe, and the hens, and the brown calf-stirk that Omeron here sacrificed for my sake.'

" Then the Countess, for it was she herself, came down from her grand seat, and held out her hand, all sparkling with rings, to us, just as her husband had done, and took little Neil from Omeron and kissed him, and kept him in her arms, so that anyone could see she was a real mother.

" Then, seeing that I was ready to sink with weariness and fatigue, she called two of her serving-women and bade them take me and the bairns away to their part of the Castle, and see that we had bite and sup, and warm water to wash ourselves with, which was the thing we needed most. And she gave orders that after we were washed and fed we were to go straight to bed.

"And oh! Donald, it was like heaven. To get into a warm, clean room, where we felt that we were safe, with a fire on the hearth, and a great pot of hot water to wash the bairns with and to bathe my own tired and blistered feet. And to get clean things to put on, and white bread (a thing I had rarely seen in my life before) to eat, and milk for the bairns to drink, and a taste of Malvoisie wine for myself, and then to snuggle down in a grand warm bed, and to sleep and sleep, and never waken till the sun was high in the heavens next day, and to find a lassie with a bicker of porridge and milk at my bedside! Me who had never been waited on before in my life!

"And that was not all, for when I was up and dressed in the braw new clothes that I found lying by my bedside, the Countess herself came in and took me out with the bairns to where Omeron and the Earl were waiting—the Earl very pleased-like and happy, and Omeron looking somewhat uneasy and red in the face. For it was a big stride, from

being a poor and humble deer-keeper who lived
in a little poverty-stricken hut at the back of beyond,
to being a real laird, with a well-built stone house
and four merks of land of his own.

"Yet that was what had befallen your grandfather,
and all because he had shown common Christian
charity to a wounded man. For the Earl then and
there installed us in this house, which happened to
be empty, and made over four merks of land to
Omeron and his descendants for all time coming.
There were some bits of furniture in the house when
we came to it, and a cheery fire burning, and a
dinner set out on the table, ready for us to sit down
to. We hardly knew how to stammer out our
thanks, and even when the Earl and her Ladyship
had gone, and we had eaten our dinner, which was
a by-ordinar good one, I could not believe I was
not in a dream till I went out to the byre, and there
was Crummie lying as contented and settled-in-like
as if she had been there all her life. Then I knew
that it was true."

V

MURIELLA OF CAWDOR

It was drawing towards Christmas in the year 1498, and the snow lay white and deep round the ancient Castle of Cawdor in the county of Nairn. Winter had come early that year, and what with the prolonged cold and the short days and long dark nights of that northern region, a deep gloom seemed to have settled down over the countryside.

For times were hard for most folk, and this year little help might be expected from the Castle, for the young Thane of Cawdor, to whom his father, who was still alive, had handed over the estate, had died in August, and his brothers, Andrew and Alex and Hugh of that name, were different men, cruel, hard-hearted, and stern, and woe betide Strathnairn if one of them succeeded to the earldom.

That was the fear that worked on every poor man's heart, for Thane John had left no heir, although there were hopes that the empty arms of his widow, the Lady Isabella, would be filled by a little son or daughter ere Yuletide came.

So, great was the relief and joy that spread through the countryside when, on the Eve of St. Thomas, just four days before Christmas, news was carried from the Castle that a baby girl had been born, who, according to her father's will, inherited the rich domain of Cawdor.

"'Tis a pity 'tis not a boy," said old Euphan the nurse to her crony, Eppie the byre-woman, when she carried the milk into the great kitchen. "But 'tis a fine lass, healthy and well made, and wi' the bonniest crop o' red curls that I have seen for many a day. She favours her mother's folk, the Roses of Kelrivock—they are a' red in the head. But what matters it how she is coloured, so long as she is here. Gin she had never been born, we would a' have been at the tender mercy of her Uncle Andrew, who is a wild and merciless man, and I say it who kens—for I nursed him mysel', as I did all his brothers."

"Aye, he would fain have ruled in Thane John's place," replied Eppie, "and doubtless at this moment he has little love in his heart either for the bairn or for her mother. But bairns have the knack of finding their way into the hardest heart; and when once he gets over his disappointment, Sir Andrew will be as fond of the bairn as any of us."

And the wise old woman's words proved true. Little Muriella grew up a strong and healthy child, who ran about the old Castle and its courtyard like

6

a beam of sunshine, her red curls bobbing in the wind. And, by the time she was three years old, there was not a man or woman among her retainers who would not have laid down their lives for their little lady.

I say there was not a man who would not have laid down his life for her—but here I am mistaken. For her Uncle Andrew, although he was kind enough to the child, and would carry her on his shoulder, and tell her stories about the grim old Castle that was her home, still cast longing eyes on the fair heritage of which she was the inheritor. He even went the length of travelling to Edinburgh and craving an audience of the King, in which he pointed out to the monarch how dangerous a thing it was for a girl to be heiress to such a large estate, and how much better it would be if his niece were pensioned off with a sufficient sum of money to enable her to be brought up according to her station, leaving him to become Thane and master of the vast estate of Cawdor.

But King James only laughed at him. " Na, na," he cried; " your brother John took good care to tie up his heritage safely for his heir, whether lad or lassie. The bairn was to be a ward of the Crown, which makes the King of Scotland, and no other, her lawful guardian. And as I, through my manifold responsibilities, cannot give time to the

matter, I have appointed her grandfather on her
mother's side—to wit, Sir Hugh Rose of Kelrivock
—and my good cousin, Archibald, Earl of Argyll,
to be her tutors until such time as she be of age to
take a husband and, with his help, manage her own
affairs."

Andrew of Cawdor bowed low and left the Royal
presence. After such a reproof there was nothing
else for him to do ; but he retraced his steps to the
north with black anger in his heart, and a firm
resolve that, come what might, Muriella and her
money should be kept in the family.

He was an unmarried man, and, if it had been
possible, he would have waited for twelve years or
so and married her himself, but that was forbidden
by all the laws of God and Holy Kirk. But Hugh,
his next brother, was married, and had a son but
two years younger than the little girl. They two
might wed in days to come, for the Kirk would
allow cousins to marry.

And as he formed the plan in his mind, Sir Andrew
grew calmer and more contented.

But he was not the only schemer. Across the
river, in Kelrivock Tower, Sir Hugh Rose, who had
just received the King's mandate appointing him
one of the young heiress's guardians, was plotting
also. He had a grandson, young Walter Rose,
just a few years older than his granddaughter.

They were cousins, but, like Sir Andrew, he hugged to his heart the thought that the Church did not forbid such unions, so what was to prevent them marrying ? Then the estate of Cawdor would, in the future, be joined to that of Kelrivock, and his great-grandson would inherit both.

Sir Hugh rubbed his hands as he thought of the coming years, and, calling to his wife, he instructed her to send an invitation at once to their daughter Isabella at Cawdor, asking her to come to Kelrivock Tower on a long visit and bring little Muriella along with her.

" If they have to be man and wife, the sooner Walter and she get to know each other the better," he said slyly. " Hugh of Cawdor has a laddie also, and we have no wish that she gets too sib* with him."

Meanwhile, far away over the mountains, the great Earl of Argyll, who was at that time all-powerful in Scotland, was also holding a family council at Inveraray Castle. And more than a family council, for he had summoned the heads of the chief branches of his clan.

He, too, had received the King's mandate of guardianship. " She will do for one of my own sons," he said. " Archie, my namesake, will have the earldom here, and be Head of the Clan when

* Sib, friendly.

I am gone, but it will be a good down-sitting
for John.   He is ten years older than the
wench, but that will not matter, and he is gentle-
natured and good-hearted, and will make her
a kind husband.   Sir John Campbell of Cawdor!
'Tis quite a well-sounding name.   Weel! The
sooner the lassie is taken out of the hands of her
uncles and her mother's folk the better.   Doubtless
they will be plotting to marry her off to some
hanger - on of their own.   I have the King's
authority, and I will act upon it.   She must be
brought to Inveraray and reared in her future
husband's home.   So I depute thee, my kinsman
Inverliver, to gang over to Cawdor with thy
clansmen, and bring back the maiden, alive, if
thou canst get her; dead, if there be no other
way."

" She would not be muckle good to thee dead, my
Lord;" said Sir Niall Campbell of Inverliver with
a laugh, " no lad can wed a dead bride."

" Would she no?" replied the Earl shortly.
" It is a far cry from Strathnairn to the land of the
Campbells, and whatever happens, Muriella of
Cawdor can never die as long as there is a red-
headed lassie of her own age on either side of Loch
Awe."

'Twas a lightly spoken word, but it was caught up
and passed on as a jest from one to another, and the

Earl would have been sore angered and astonished had he known that it was repeated both in Cawdor Castle and Kelrivock Tower long ere Niall Campbell of Inverliver had collected his band of men.

Meanwhile, all unaware of the stir which her small presence in the world was creating, the little Muriella played about peacefully in the Castle and park at Cawdor, or in her grandfather's Tower at Kelrivock, her faithful old nurse being always at her side. When night fell, and she was tired of play, the old woman would take her on her lap, and by the light of the fire would tell her many a story about the fairy folk, and about elves and gnomes, and draglin hoglins, until the child, who did not know what fear was, would tiptoe to the window and stand looking out at the moonlight, hoping to see some of these ferlies with her own eyes.

But the story she loved most of all was the story of how the massive Tower of Cawdor, in one of the turrets of which she sat, came to be built on its present situation. Over and over again Euphan had to repeat the story of how the first Thane of Cawdor, having obtained lands on which to build his Castle, was sore torn in his mind as to the best site to choose; and how, while he was still uncertain, a dream was vouchsafed to him, as dreams were vouchsafed to holy men of old. In it he was directed to load an ass with gold, and to turn it out to wander whither it would. He was to follow, and to build his Castle on the spot where the animal at last lay down to rest.

The Thane carried out the instructions given in the dream. He borrowed a donkey from one of his vassals, hung a bag of gold across its neck, and turned it out to wander on the moorland. For an hour or two it roamed uneasily about, nibbling at a thistle here and a thistle there; then at last, tired by the weight of its unwonted burden, it lay down to rest under a hawthorn tree on the edge of a steep bank overlooking a swift-flowing stream.

The Thane accepted the omen, and built his Tower so as to enclose the hawthorn tree, and nothing pleased little Muriella better than to persuade Euphan to light a cruisie, and, taking her by the hand, go down the flight of dark stairs to the dungeon, and show her the old, gnarled trunk of the hawthorn tree, which still pierced both floor and roof of that dismal chamber.

The little maiden loved to turn the story into a real game, and, with Euphan's help, would fill a bag with pebbles from the edge of the river, and lay it across the back of the tiny sheltie, which her Uncle Hugh had given her to ride, and, letting go his rein, would watch breathlessly where he would lie down. But the sheltie, albeit he was old and staid, as befitted the steed of a four-year-old maiden, always flung his heels in the air, and tossed off the bag, and trotted gaily about the park without showing the slightest sign of wanting to take a rest, greatly to the disappointment of his little mistress.

One sunny morning in late September, Muriella and her sheltie were playing this game. She had just been a ride to the harvest field, Euphan walking beside her holding Rorie's rein, and after watching the sheaves of yellow corn being piled on the great stack at one end of the field, they had turned to go home. As soon as they entered the park Euphan had lifted the little girl from the saddle, and had replaced her by the familiar bag of stones. But Rorie, instead of trotting about from thistle to thistle as he was supposed to do, had cantered away in the direction of his stable, as hard as his legs would carry him.

" Eh, but the greedy beast kens that it is time for its midday feed of corn," cried Euphan, " which is a sign that the clock has chappit twelve, and that your denner will be on the table also, my doo. Come and let us run, else will your lady mother be angered. For your uncles have gone to the tryst at Nairn, and she gave orders that you were to take your meals with her today."

So hand in hand they set off, the old woman and the little child, at their best pace across the park. But they did not go very far. All of a sudden their way was blocked by a band of horsemen, who appeared by magic, as it were, out of a thick clump of trees which bordered the path. They were the dreaded Campbells from the west country, Euphan could see that from the colour of their plaids, and, scenting danger to her charge at once, she picked the child up in her arms, and faced the strangers like a stag at bay.

" Who are ye ?" she said, " and what do ye want ? For if ye want Andrew or Hugh of Cawdor, they are away at the tryst at Nairn, an' will not be back before the darkening. Meanwhile, if ye please, let me pass, for it is time that this bairn here had her dinner."

" We can let you pass, my good woman," replied a tall, fine-looking man, who, by the richness of his dress, and the silver-handled dirk that he wore, was clearly the leader of the band, " but the bairn must go with us. I am Niall Campbell of Inverliver, and I am come from the head of my clan, whom the King hath appointed tutor to the Lady Muriella, to take her for safe keeping to his Castle of Inveraray. As for her uncles being at Nairn, that is the very reason why we are here today, so that there may be no argument about the matter. So hand up the bairn to Jock here, without any more ado. He has ten of his own, and kens fine how to look after a little wench on a rough journey. Ye needna be feared," he added, as Euphan gazed wildly at the great bearded Highlander on the big black horse who rode behind Inverliver, and who was even now stretching out his arms to take her darling. " Jock has a bottle of milk in his pocket and a bag of cakes at his saddle-bow, and when we have put twenty miles between us and Cawdor, we'll draw rein for a minute and give the bairn a piece."

Poor Euphan ! She knew it was hopeless to try to resist, much less to break through the ranks of horsemen and gain the Castle. But her love was strong, and her brain worked quickly. What was it she had heard that the Campbells had said ? That once Muriella was in their hands, she would never die as long as there was a red-haired lass on either side of Loch Awe.

" By my faith !" said the dauntless old woman to herself, " but they'll have no chance of changing my little queen for ony other lassie. For I'll set my mark on her. Living or dead, there will only be one Muriella of Cawdor."

" Wait a minute, my Lord, till I wrap my shawl round her. Her cloak is but thin, and the wind would blow through it if ye travel fast. Forgive me, my lamb, but it's because of my love for thee," she murmured, as she tore her old tartan shawl off her shoulders, and wrapped it round the bewildered child, smothering her with kisses as she did so. Then a sudden turmoil arose. Muriella began to kick and scream as if she were bewitched, and the old nurse, as if she could bear it no longer, thrust the struggling child up into Jock Campbell's arms, and turned and sped towards the Castle, sobbing and moaning as she did so, the horsemen making way for her to pass through their ranks.

" Muffle the bairn in your plaid, or tie the shawl over her head, Jock," cried Niall Campbell sharply, " else will her cries rouse the place. Come on, men; we have got the prize, so let us get as far on our road as we can ere word reach Andrew and Hugh that their house has been plundered and the bairn ta'en."

So rowells were plunged in the horses' sides, and the band of reavers galloped swiftly out of the park and across the level plain which lay between the Castle and the hills, the countryfolk scattering like sheep as they passed, for word had flown from mouth to mouth that the riders were Campbells, and that it was not safe to bar their way.

When they had ridden for a couple of hours, their leader called a halt. " We can give the beasts a breathing-space," he said, " and take a bite to ourselves, and let Jock here feed his charge. Gin the bairn had no dinner, she must be gey wauf*

* Faint.

now wi' fright and hunger.   And, after all, my orders were to steal her, not to starve her."

And ". gey wauf" poor little Muriella proved to be, when her bearded guardian swung himself down from his horse, and with clumsy but accustomed fingers undid the shawl which he had wound so closely round her.

" Dod, but the bairn's in a dwaum !" he exclaimed anxiously, as he saw Muriella's white face and closed eyes; and what have we here ?" and he lifted in dismay her scarlet cloak and white wincey frock which were all stained and wet with blood. " She canna hae come against the point o' my dirk when I lifted her up," he went on, carefully examining the little girl, who seemed only half conscious.

" It's her hand," said Inverliver, who stood looking on, feeling, if the truth must be told, somewhat concerned.

Big Jock lifted the little hand in his, and then it was clear to all what had happened. In desperation at the thought that if aught should happen to the child she loved so dearly, some other red-headed wench would be put in her place, old Euphan had set a mark on her which no one else was likely to imitate, *for the top of her little finger was gone*.

" Faix ! but the old woman must have had the teeth of a rat," cried Inverliver, " and she has not spared the bairn. But I admire her for it. She has made it difficult for Muriella to be lost sight of. But for pity's sake, Jock, tie up the wound, for the lassie has lost a deal of blood. And try to get her to take a sup of milk, else she is like to die on our hands."

Jock obeyed, very tenderly and skilfully, thinking of his own little maidens at home, and before the order was given to remount, a little of Muriella's colour had returned to her cheeks, and she was sufficiently recovered to begin to cry out for Euphan.

" I'm taking you to her, my bonny bird," said Jock, quite regardless, so long as he comforted and reassured the child, of how many lies he was laying on his soul.

More time had been wasted by this delay than had been intended, and, just as his men were mounting, Inverliver's keen eyes saw a body of horsemen advancing rapidly through the cornfields, apparently in pursuit.

His forehead wrinkled at the sight of them, and a look of grim determination settled on his face. " Andrew and Hugh have got the news quicker than I counted on," he said; " they must have been early home from Nairn. And we are late—so late that a bairn's little finger may weel cost us the lives of many a buirdly man. For the Cawdors are bitter fighters.   But be that as it may, we must keep what we have got.   Give me the bairn's red cloak and bonnet—the shawl must do her till she lands at Inveraray.   Here !   Five of you be off with big Jock, and never halt or draw rein till the gates of the Castle are shut behind you, and you have given the lassie into the Earl's own hands.   Tell him that Inverliver and his sons stopped behind to bar the way."

Big Jock did not waste words.   Stripping Muriella of her outdoor garments, he wrapped her tightly in the shawl, and, throwing his own plaid over her as he settled her firmly in the crook of his arm, he turned his horse's face to a gap in the hills, and, followed by five of the clan, galloped swiftly away.

Meanwhile the Laird of Inverliver had picked up a little stook of corn, and, to the amazement of his followers, was hastily dressing it up in Muriella's clothes.   When the red cloak was fastened round it, and the little white cotton bonnet tied round its crown of oats, it looked, at a distance, very like a living child.

" Here !"—and he flung it in haste to one of the riders, an active, fair-haired youth—" hold that in front of you, and handle it as if it were alive.   And keep to the rear, as if you were wanting to shield the bairn.   We'll keep them busy for an hour or so, and by that time big Jock will be well on his way through the pass. When once he is in the Campbell's country, or even that of Lochiel, he and his charge will be safe enough."

"Here they come, men, with Andrew and Hugh, and even the cripple Alec at their head. Stand firm, lads, and lay on right heavily."

A grim and ghastly conflict followed, for they were not only fighting for the possession of a little bit of a lassie, they were fighting for lands and siller as well. And, as we know, lands and siller mean much to men. Hither and thither the horsemen swayed, one party trying desperately to reach the horseman with the red-cloaked bairn in his arm, who hovered in the background, always just out of reach, the other party bent resolutely on preventing them breaking through.

At last, after more than an hour's desperate fighting, in which many men on either side were killed, including, it is said, seven of Inverliver's sons, that doughty warrior held his sword high above his head, a white cravat dangling from its hilt in sign of peace.

"We'll give you the bairn," he cried, "if you gather at yon side of the field, and let us gather at this, and Hector there will set her down in the middle."

Andrew of Cawdor, tired of the needless slaughter,

and glad to get Muriella back on any terms, raised his sword in agreement, and the two bodies of men grouped themselves round their leaders, and withdrew to their respective positions. Hector Campbell, at the bidding of his Chief, rode slowly forward to the middle of the field, and placed the figure which he carried carefully on the ground, with its back against a rocky boulder. Then he cantered briskly back to his companions, and, to the amazement of the men of Cawdor, the Campbells gave a shout of triumphant laughter, and, wheeling their horses round, galloped rapidly away.

The would-be Laird of Cawdor, his heart in his mouth, hurried forward to the scarlet-cloaked figure, which sat strangely still, for a terrible thought had entered his mind : was it possible his rivals had killed the wench, when they saw that it was impossible to carry her off to Inveraray ?

He was not long left in doubt. For when he knelt down and raised the white sun-bonnet, which seemed entirely to cover its wearer's face, a bunch of crushed and flattened oats met his astonished gaze. In an instant he saw what had happened. A bitter fight had been fought, and many a good man slain, all because of a sheaf of corn, dressed up in a child's clothes. Anyhow, tho' the Campbells had got her, Muriella was not dead; and with a great oath, half of rage and disappointment,

half of relief, Sir Andrew kicked the dummy half
across the field, and left it lying among the bodies
of the men who had perished in the fray.

*   *   *   *   *

And in good sooth Muriella was not dead, nor
like to die. For the Countess of Argyll was a kind,
motherly woman, who received the child, so
suddenly thrust into her care, with outstretched
arms, and with a heart full of pity for so young
a thing snatched from her natural protectors.
And as children's memories are short, and the folk
at Inveraray were kinder than the folk at home,
with the exception of old Euphan, it was no long
time before the red curls were bobbing out and in
the Castle of the Campbells as cheerfully as they had
bobbed out and in the Castle of the Cawdors.

Euphan was not there, of course, but young
John Campbell was, a gentle-natured lad, some ten
years older than the little stranger, whom from the
first he took under his boyish protection, constituting
himself her faithful knight and champion.

So the child grew to maidenhood, and she had
scarce entered her teens when John Campbell
married her, as had always been intended, sharing
with her her estates, and changing the family name
to Campbell of Cawdor. And a happy marriage
it proved to be, tho' Muriella outlived her husband,

7

and had to rule alone in the grim old Castle for many a long year.

But she had young people growing up to help her, for an ancient parchment tells us how, when she was an old woman of seventy-five, she handed over her estates to her " grandson John Campbell, and his airs male."

VI

TAM-A-LINE, THE ELFIN KNIGHT

IT was a lovely day in late autumn, some five hundred years ago. The sun was shining brightly in the courtyard of Newark Castle, that ancient hunting lodge of the Stewart Kings, which stands on the banks of the Yarrow, in the heart of Ettrick Forest.

The courtyard presented a busy sight, for the King and his nobles were mounting to ride to the chase, and a bevy of fair maidens had come down from their rooms in the tower, in order to see them depart. When the last horse had clattered out under the gateway and vanished in the forest, there was much laughing discussion as to how the long hours were to be spent ere the Royal party reappeared.

Some declared their intention of going a-hunting on their own account, some proposed a game of caitch-pelle* on the Castle green, while one fair-haired damsel announced her intention of walking along the river's bank to a lovely piece of meadow ground called Carterhaugh, where the Ettrick

* A kind of tennis.

Water joins the Yarrow, and from which their mingled waters flow on together to the Tweed.

" There are some bonny roses there, late in the year though it be," she said, " and I would fain gather a few to wear at my breast, when we dance in the hall after supper tonight."

" But 'tis to Carterhaugh we dare not go, Janet," cried Alison Murray, who lived at Elibank Castle close by, " for thine uncle hath forbidden it. 'Tis plain thou dost not live at Newark all the twelve months of the year, else wouldst thou have heard of the queer little man who haunts Carterhaugh, and frightens to death any witless wight who may chance to meet him. Tam-a-Line, folk call him, but whither he comes, or where he goes, or how he appears for a moment, then vanishes into space, no man knoweth. Doubtless he is one of the Fairy Folk, mayhap some luckless mortal who hath been stolen away and changed; but, be that as it may, 'tis certain he is not mortal now, and the sight of him drives honest folk clean out of their senses. So the Warden hath laid down a law that no maiden of Newark hath to wander that way."

" It was only yestreen that I rode from Edinburgh, in attendance upon the Queen," replied Lady Janet, who was a daughter of the Earl of March, and a relative of the Warden. " So I had not heard this strange new rule which my uncle hath been pleased to make. For strange it sounds to me, for since I was a bairn I have ever roamed through the Forest at my own sweet will whenever I have been at Newark.

"Some mortal that had been changed, thou saidst, Alison," she went on, a strange eager look coming into her great blue eyes; and seeing it, Alison Murray tried to turn the conversation, for she knew the story of Lady Janet's youth; how she had grown up from babyhood with her far-away cousin, young Gilbert Murray, and the love that had been between them even though they were little more than boy and girl.

Then of a sudden all was changed. Gilbert had ridden out hawking with his uncle, in the same Forest of Ettrick, and had suddenly vanished, no man knew how or where, and though the Forest had been searched from end to end, no trace of him, or of the horse on which he had been riding, had ever been found.

Long and bitterly the Lady Janet had mourned her companion, and 'twas said that although of late years more than one young noble had laid his heart at her feet, she would only shake her head and tell them that whatever might happen to other maidens, she could never listen to any other lover. Today, however, she had shaken off her sadness, and no one among the laughing, jesting group seemed merrier than she, as she tossed her head with its golden crown of curls in the air, and cried lightly : " Ah, well-a-day ! but I am woman grown, and cannot be held in by rules as if I were a bairn. So to Carterhaugh I go, even if it be by my lee-lane, and many a lass of you will envy me, when you see me wearing a bonny bunch of roses in my bosom."

Perhaps Lady Janet meant this as a challenge. If it were so, no one accepted it, so, kilting her green kirtle above her knees, for the grass in the meadow was wet and sodden, she set out alone to Carterhaugh.

A sweet and peaceful spot it was, to be sure : a little peninsula of land almost enclosed by the two rivers, and shaded by lofty hills. A few late flowers still lingered in the green turf underfoot, and on the wild rose trees that bordered the river banks, while among the bushes little birds twittered to each other, and high up in a fir tree a wood pigeon crooned softly to its mate.

" And this is the place that my uncle calls haunted," said Janet to herself, as she pulled down a branch of one of the rose trees and began to pick its delicately tinted blossoms. Poor man, he must be in his dotage, that he begins to believe in witches and warlocks and suchlike unchancy creatures."

Then, all of a sudden, the words died on her lips, and she let go the rose branch so suddenly that the rose leaves flew in all directions. For there at her feet was the tiniest little man she had ever seen. He was clad in white stockings, green breeches, a sky-blue coat, and a scarlet pirnie; and tho' his wee, wee feet, in their buckled shoes, rested on a tuft of grass, his head did not reach her knees.

"What art thou doing here?" cried the little mannikin in a deep-set voice. "Dost thou not know that no mortal is safe on Carterhaugh who comest hither without my leave? As to picking my roses, dire disaster will fall on anyone who is foolish enough to attempt such a thing."

"'Deed, little man, but I've come to Carterhaugh, and I have a mind to pick your roses," laughed Janet, who had now recovered from her fright and was determined that the queer little creature should not see that he had startled her. And she raised her hand again to grasp the branch.

The strange little being made no further objection, but stood looking on quietly while Janet filled her hands and her apron with roses, then turned to go home. Then he laid one of his tiny hands on the edge of her gown.

"Sit down here a moment, lady," he pleaded, "and grudge not an hour of thy time to one of the Fairy Folk."

There was such an anxious expression on the little man's face, and such a wistful look in his eyes, that Janet complied, even tho' she was now feeling a little cold and lonely, and would not have been sorry to find herself safe within the walls of Newark Tower.

She grew more and more uneasy when she found the tiny gay-clad goblin, for so he seemed to be, actually trying to make love to her, and yet some spell seemed to lie over her, for she felt constrained to listen patiently; and even when he made the astounding request that she should marry him, she seemed to have no power to refuse, but found herself promising to do so, if only he would assure her that he was a christened soul, and not a spirit nor a goblin, as he appeared to be.

" Fear not, lady," he said—and there was a note of triumph in his voice—" for I am a mortal like thyself, and like thyself, I was carried as a bairn to Holy Kirk, and sained* like other folk. The Fairy Folk call me Tam-a-Line now, Gilbert was I named then. I have often played with thee, Janet, and ridden with thee, and hunted with thee. Dost thou not mind how thou rodest the white pony and I the brown, and how we vowed we would be man and wife when we were old enough to wed.

" Thou art not wedded yet, Janet," he went on, peering with his funny little eyes at the wedding finger on her left hand.

* Blessed.

"Nay, I'm not wedded yet, nor ever will be," replied Janet in bewilderment, "unless 'tis to Gilbert Murray, the lad you're speaking of. But we've looked on him as dead for the last seven years, and as for thou being him, I just cannot believe it."

"Oh! who and what art thou?" she broke out passionately. "Tell me the truth, unless thou wouldest break my heart. If thou art Gilbert, as thou sayest, where hast thou been all these weary years, and what hath befallen thee, that thou appearest in this guise?"

"'Tis soon told," said the little man, coming closer to her, and placing his tiny hand upon her larger one.

"Thou rememberest, dear heart, how, when I was a lad of fourteen, my uncle, the Keeper of the Forest, sent for me to keep him company, and to teach me to hunt and to hawk. It befell one day when we were riding out that a strange icy wind sprang up in the north, and, though it was but October, brought with it a griming of snow. It seemed as if the chill went round my heart, for I fell into a dwaum, and for a space of time I remembered no more.

"When I awoke I found myself in Fairyland, under that green knowe that rises in the haugh yonder. The Queen of that land had caught me as I fell from my horse, and had carried me swiftly thither, and there I have lived ever since, among the Little Folk. It has been on the whole a happy life, for we fairies are free from both sickness and pain. We come and go as we like, on land, or on sea, or in air. We can leave our bodies at will, and return to them again. We can change into any shape we choose, and can make ourselves so tiny that we can sleep in a nutshell, or so light that we can ride on a sunbeam. We can shelter from the rain in a rosebud, or fly from place to place on the wind. But ever are we the slaves of the Queen of Fairyland, and tho' she is so beautiful and gracious, she never means to let us go."

" But I'll never let thee go either, now I've found thee again," cried the Lady Janet. And if anyone had seen the look on her face at that moment, they would have known she was in deadly earnest.

" It is not that I have such a desire to be done with Fairyland, Janet," went on the little man rather wistfully; "but I'm feared, Janet, I'm feared."

His voice sank lower, and he crept closer to his lady-love, as if for protection. " Fairyland is very bonny, Janet, and we would be very happy were it not for one awful dread that is aye hanging over us. For tho' our Queen owes no allegiance to mortal man, and can defy him at her will, there is one to whom she has to bow, the Evil One himself.

"And once in seven years she has, as it were, to pay teinds to him, just as we pay teinds to Holy Kirk on earth, and the teinds, Janet, the teinds, is a nice fat goblin, the fairest and the fattest she can find. And although I'm not very big, Janet, I'm fat and well-favoured. So that is why I'm feared, in case her choice should fall on me."

"Now Heaven and the Saints forfend!" exclaimed the horrified lady, crossing herself in haste on bosom and lip and brow. "If the Evil One is master of the Fairy Queen, there is One mightier than the Evil One, and in His Name I will defy them both.

"Tell me, Gilbert, for I will call thee by thy christened name, what can I do to break the spell that binds thee?"

At these brave words the little man's courage rose again.

"The Saints shield thee, Janet!" he cried, "for if thou wilt assay it at all, thou must do it tonight. For, as thou knowest, this is Hallow-e'en, the Eve of All-Hallow's Day. And on this night, at midnight, all the fairies are abroad in their thousands, witches and warlocks, elves and gnomes, goblins and hobgoblins—yes, and the Queen of Fairyland herself, attended by her retinue.

" I will be there, Janet, in her company, and if thou wilt be brave enough to attempt to rescue me, thou must be at Mary's Cross on the heath at the stroke of twelve, with a flagon of Holy Water in thy hand which, when the Fairy Hosts appear, thou must sprinkle in a circle round thee, to keep the Powers of Darkness away."

" But how shall I know thee, Tam-a-Line? For methinks the Queen will have other knights as well."

" That hath she," quoth Tam-a-Line, " thousands of them, and they ride in different companies. Thou must not meddle with the first or second company of riders—let them pass in peace—but when the third band approaches, clad all in green, then be ready, for that is the Queen's procession, and I will ride behind her.

" Thou wilt know me by my milk-white steed, and by the star in the coronet which I shall wear. That star hath ever been my hope, even in Fairyland, for it marks me out from all the rest for a christened man. Beside these tokens, I shall uncover my left hand, so that the moon, if she be risen, will shine upon my bare flesh.

" But hark'ee, Janet, when thou hast pulled me from my horse, and hast me safe in thine arms, think not that all is done. Na, na, men do not escape from the gramarye* of the Little Folk so easily

* Gramarye, magic.

as that. There are many other charms they will throw over me to prevent thee from winning my freedom. They'll turn me in thy arms from a little man into an adder, and then into an asp. And if thou dost not shrink and cast me away, I'll be turned into a blazing faggot, and into a red-hot bar of iron. But if thy courage lasts, and thou wilt but hold on, no harm can come to thee, not even a scar or a burn.

"Dip me first in milk and then in water, and the fire will be quenched, and thou wilt find thyself holding a wriggling eel, which, if thou dost not let it go, will soon turn into a toad. Cast not the loathly thing away, for by-and-by it will exchange its ugliness for the softness of a dove, which will grow bigger and bigger till it is changed into a snow-white swan. Cast thy cloak over the bird and it will vanish, leaving in its stead my mortal body, and I will stand at thy side once more, a knight of whom, I hope, thou wilt not be ashamed." With these words the queer little mannikin vanished, and Janet found herself alone in the gloaming, a bunch of roses in her hand.

She sped home to Newark Castle in breathless haste, and that night she danced as if she were fey, with a colour in her cheeks and a light in her eyes that made the hearts of her partners leap within them when they glanced down at her.

When the dance was over, and everyone had gone to bed, anyone lingering outside the Castle might have seen a little postern door slowly open and a dark cloaked figure step out. It looked to right and left, then, noiselessly shutting the postern after it, vanished among the trees.

It was the Lady Janet, and she was heavily laden. For she carried beneath her cloak a flagon of Holy Water, which she had sent her own bower maid to obtain from the priest who served the little chapel on the hillside further up the valley, another flagon of milk, and two dishes, which she meant to fill, according to her lover's instructions, the one with milk, the other with water.

Oh, but it was an eerie walk, through the wood and across the barren heather, all the way to Mary's Cross, and more than once her heart almost failed her. But she persevered, and by midnight she had reached the Cross, and had filled one basin with milk and another with water. Then she seated herself on an outcrop of rock and waited patiently.

Half an hour went by in an unearthly silence, then far in the distance a bright twinkling light, like a will-o'-the-wisp appeared, now wavering to this side, now to that, in its strange uncertain course, but ever drawing nearer and nearer. Janet sprang to her feet, and as she did so, the cold north wind rose and swept over the heather with a long-drawn sigh, like a soul in pain. This was followed by a blast of fairy music, mingled with the ring of horses' harness and the jingling of champing bits.

The music was so strange and unearthly that Janet wondered how it was produced, but soon the Fairy Hosts passed by, tripping and dancing along on the heath, or riding on beautiful horses, covered with rich trappings, which were hung with tinkling bells. Almost all the Little Folk were joining in the orchestra, some piping shrilly through pipes cut from the slender stems of oat-straw, some playing on hemlock stalks, some on bigger reeds cut from marshes and bogs.

They were massed together in groups, in some sort of prearranged order, and Janet waited calmly until the first two parties passed by.

Her heart began to beat quickly, however, and her breath came in little gasps as the third company approached, for the moon had now risen, and by its light she could see, even at a distance, that the riders were clad all in green. They were led by the most beautiful woman she had ever seen, and it did not need the sight of her rich dress and the wonderful trappings of her horse to tell her that this was indeed the Queen of the Fairies.

Her redingote was of soft green silk, the colour of meadow grass in spring, and her yellow hair covered her shoulders like a golden veil. On her head she wore a wreath of roses twisted in and out with a fillet of gold. Her saddle was of ivory, and the girths that fastened it were of fine-spun silk.

Her bridle was made of twisted strands of gold and silver, hung with golden bells, while her stirrups were formed of clear crystal, studded with pearls. She carried a bow, and stuck in her girdle was a sheaf of arrows, while from a silver cord round her neck dangled a richly chased gold and silver hunting-horn. She blew this at intervals as she rode along, and its shrill notes sounded and resounded over the deserted moorland and echoed among forest trees. At other times she laughed and sang and threw merry jests over her shoulders to the company of eldritch riders behind her.

Though she was very beautiful, there was something sinister and forbidding about her, and, as she drew near, Janet opened her flagon of Holy Water and sprinkled it in haste in a ring all round her.

She had just finished doing so when the riders came up to her. Apparently their eyes were holden, for they did not see her, and swept by proudly, a strange, unearthly company.

First went by some riders on black horses, but Janet paid no heed to them; then went by those whose steeds were brown. Still she waited motionless within her hallowed circle. At last the rider she was looking for appeared.

Perched high up on a great white horse came Tam-a-Line, wearing his green breeches and sky-blue coat. But the scarlet pirnie was gone, and in its place was a golden coronet, in the front of which twinkled and glittered a burning star.

Twitching his bridle rein as if by accident, he drew his horse to the very edge of the sacred circle, and Janet, stepping forward, reached out her arms, and, snatching him from his saddle, drew back to its centre, where she was safe from any witchery which the Queen of the Fairies might try to throw over her.

Tam-a-Line's white steed, startled by the girl's sudden appearance, galloped away over the moor, and as it passed through their ranks riderless, and with its bridle trailing, the Fairy Queen and her followers realized with anger and chagrin what had happened. With cries of rage and disappointment they vanished in an instant from mortal sight, though by a cold feeling in her bones, Janet knew that they were still around her, shrunk in a moment into their original size, and hidden under mushrooms or toadstools, or nestling under the leaves of the trees, or among the tangled roots of the brown and shrivelled heather.

But though her very marrow was chilled by the

eeriness of it all, Janet held fast to her lover, determined to win him back to mortal form and human
life.

It all came about as he had foretold. First he
was turned into a smooth, wriggling adder, which
twisted and turned about in Janet's arms until she
shuddered with fear ; then the adder was turned into
a slimy asp, from which she would fain have shrunk
away in disgust.

Soon she held a blazing faggot, which, however,
had no power to scorch her ; and this turned into
a red-hot bar of iron, which felt as if it would burn
her fingers to the bone. But, as she looked round
desperately for help, feeling that she must throw the
molten thing away, her eyes fell on the dish of milk
and the dish of water, which, according to Tam-a-
Line's instructions, she had prepared and placed
ready on the ground at her feet.

Plunging the glowing iron first in one, then in
the other, she found it transformed into a spotted
toad, which almost jumped out of her hands. This
in turn was changed into an eel, which was so
smooth and slippery that she had much ado to hold
it. Just as she was wondering what other horror
was in store for her, the wriggling creature was
transformed into a gentle cushie-dow or wood
pigeon, which nestled close against her breast
and crooned softly up in her face.

The relief was so great that tears came into the brave girl's eyes, and she was almost sorry when the grey dove grew bigger and bigger and whiter and whiter, until a magnificent white swan rested in her arms.

The creature was so big she could not hold him, and a little anguished cry escaped her lips as he flew to the ground, for she feared that he might escape and all her courage and fortitude prove of no avail. In her distress she slipped off her cloak and threw it over the beautiful bird in the hope that that might prevent it flying away.

But she need not have been afraid, for no sooner did the stately creature's feet touch the ground, than he slowly faded out of sight, and in his place stood a tall and stately knight, clad in Lincoln green, with a bow in his hand and a horn slung across his back.

It was Tam-a-Line grown up, and yet it was Gilbert Murray, grown up also, but with the same kindly face and merry eyes that Janet had loved ever since she was a tiny child.

She flung herself into his arms, and he held her tight, little heeding the angry and disappointed cry that came from the depths of a whinbush close at hand.

" Now woe is me, for I have lost my bonniest knight," wailed the voice, " the goodliest lad and the pick o' the lave. Had I but known, Tam-a-Line, mortal maiden could have such courage, I would have picked out thine eyes and filled the sockets with wood, and torn out thine heart and replaced it with a stone, ere ever I let thee ride out with me this night. And as to my teinds to the Evil One, gin he would have sided with me, so that I could have kept thee safe in Fairyland, I would gladly have paid him sevenfold what he asked."

Gilbert Murray only laughed. " 'Tis my late mistress, the Queen," he said, " who is loth to part with one of her subjects. 'Twas ill work for her, but lucky for me, that a mortal maiden *was* brave enough to meet the Powers of Darkness and brave their spells. For, once vanquished, they can never again have any power over me—no, not if the Fairy Queen tried for twice ten hundred years.

" But see, the dawn is breaking, Janet, and the sun is shining through the mist. Let us hasten back to Newark Tower, where the other maidens will dance at a wedding ere many days be past."

VII

ELIZABETH OF DUART

In the whole region of Argyll there was no lovelier maiden to be found than the Lady Elizabeth Campbell, the motherless daughter of the Chief of the Clan. She was born and brought up at the Castle of Inveraray, and as she grew to womanhood many were the Scottish nobles who sought her hand.

But she would listen to none of them, for her heart was already given to a young Englishman, Sir Malise Graeme, who was a friend of her brother, Lord Lorne, and who had often visited the Castle.

They were not openly betrothed, however, nor did her father, the Earl, look with favour on the friendship, for he would rather that his daughter married a son of some neighbouring chieftain, who might, through the connection thus formed, become an ally of the Campbells.

So when a quarrel broke out between his clan and the Macleans of Mull, and after one bloody battle in which the Macleans were vanquished, it was like as if bitter strife might rage between them, the crafty Earl thought there was no harm in making his fair young daughter a peace-offering. He suggested to Lachlan Maclean, Lord of Duart, who was the Head of the Clan (and also a widower who wanted a wife), that he should wed his daughter, and thereafter put all thoughts of malice and revenge out of his head. Lachlan jumped at the offer. He was a middle-aged man, famed for his great strength and his dour temper, and one or two maidens to whom he had paid his suit would have none of him.

So the chance of marrying the only daughter of the great MacCallum More, as the Earl was called, was not to be lost.

In vain poor Elizabeth sobbed and cried, and begged her father not to force her to marry a man whom she both disliked and feared; the Earl had made up his mind that for the peace of the two clans the marriage must take place, and he would not listen to her.

So the poor girl was married to the sullen-faced, red-bearded Lord of Duart, and was carried off by him over the sea to his Castle in Mull. The only member of the clan who accompanied her was her old nurse, Mairi, and, to her dismay, when they arrived on the island, her husband forbade her to have any communication whatever with her old home.

Of course, Elizabeth felt very lonely and sad, but

she had a sweet, dutiful nature, and she tried to make the best of things, and to fill up her time by visiting any of her husband's retainers who were old or sick, and teaching them how to cook nourishing food and how to dress wounds and sores. And because she did this, although she was loved and honoured by the crofters to whom she ministered, other people became jealous of her popularity, and whispered to each other that she must be in league with the Unseen Powers, because every sick person she tended began at once to mend.

But Elizabeth heard none of these murmurs, or, if she did, she paid little attention to them, for a great hope was rising in her mind, which was realized when a baby boy lay in her arms. With a little child to love and care for, her empty heart was filled again, and she had no time to brood over her old life. Late one evening Mairi beckoned to her at the nursery door. "There's mair here than the bairn," she whispered; "there's them that have come a long way to see thee. So go in and speak to them, and I'll watch here, and if danger threatens I'll let this log of wood fall—nobody can suspect anything from that—and the strangers can hide themselves behind my box bed; we've moved it forward a bit, so that there may be room, and thou canst sit down and rock the cradle."

With a beating heart, Elizabeth opened the door, and there in the gleaming firelight she saw her brother Lorne and her old sweetheart Malise Graeme. With a little cry of joy she threw herself into her brother's arms, then turned and offered her hand to his friend. For Elizabeth was a loyal woman, and mindful of her wifely dignity.

" Oh ! how did you come?" she cried, " and what is thine errand ? Are you not afraid of your lives? For in spite of the fact that I am his wife, Maclean seems set against the Campbells, and hath both forbidden me to send any message, and threatens to kill any man who bears the name who dares to set foot in Mull."

" We came because we had heard no word of thee since the day thou settest sail from Inveraray," replied Lord Lorne. " My father hath waited till he could wait no longer, fearing that some ill had befallen thee. By St. Columb, I trow his conscience is never done troubling him because he forced thee to marry that ill-conditioned man of thine. He was keen to come over himself, but he could not come without a following of men, and that would but have stirred up strife again. So as Graeme and I were hunting in Morven, and came in the chase nearby the sea, the coast of Mull seemed so near, and thou so dear to both of us, we e'en hired a cobble and rowed ourselves across. We left it hidden among the rocks, down-by at the shore, so if we are discovered we can jump from the window and run for our .lives. But hark'ee dear heart, if thou art not happy here, or if Maclean is not good to thee, we will take thee with us, and thou shalt be our queen once more at Inveraray."

Elizabeth shook her head, though tears of longing rose in her eyes as she thought of her old home.

" I cannot leave my son," she said proudly, " and it would not be just nor right to take him with me. So tell my father I am well, and that I have given him a grandson, and maybe, in the days to come, I may once more visit Argyll and bring my son with me."

They had no more time to talk, for Mairi came hurrying in to say that Maclean was coming home from the chase, and that if the two strangers wished to escape unnoticed they had better go at once.

But it chanced as they were stealing down the brae face to the sea, old Duncan the cowherd saw them, and watched them get into their boat and pull out from the shore. Duncan was one of those who had no love for his mistress—she had spoken sharply to him when she had come on him kicking a day-old calf, threatening that if she ever found him doing the same again he would be dismissed. So he went straight to Allan Maclean of Lochtarish, and told him that the Lady Elizabeth had had visitors from over the sea, and that he was sure they were her own kith and kin, for they had headed their boat straight for the hills of Morven.

Now Allan Maclean had once been a prisoner in the hands of the Campbells, and although at last they had given him his liberty, he hated them with a deep, burning hatred. So he sent messages to the smaller chieftains of the clan to meet him when the moon was full, in a great cave in the rocks down by the sea, as he had something important to say to them. Full of curiosity, they assembled as he bade them, and indignation rose in their hearts as he laid his story before them. For Lochtarish was unscrupulous as well as wily, and he led the chiefs to believe that Lady Elizabeth was double-faced, and that she was in league with the Campbells, and that spies were coming and going between Morven and Mull.

" Are we going to be made a laughing-stock and a byword?" he cried. " A couple of months syne, when I was out with my men in our biggest boat, a cobble passed us with a couple of Argyll's gillies in it. And they gibed and jeered at us, saying that we dare not touch them, for the Macleans had been completely cowed by the Campbells."

" Shame on us," muttered his listeners, " to let such a state of affairs go on. For as long as the Mistress of the Castle is a Campbell and the Laird

is under her thumb, we dare not anger them in
any way, and they will come and go unheeded, till
they know all our defences and the easy places
to land ; and someday they will come in force, and
before we know where we are, what the men in the
cobble said will be true, and we will be their
vassals."

So they wrought themselves into a fury, and, as
ill luck would have it, Maclean himself, who had
been walking on the sands, and who had heard their
excited voices, entered the cave at that moment, and
looked round in astonishment at such a gathering.

Then they vented their wrath on him, telling him
that his wife was a traitress, how she was in league
with her own people, and was harbouring spies
in secret in the Castle during the night. They told
him he must choose between his wife and his position
as Lord of Duart and Chieftain of the Clan.

" Maclean of Benlora would make as good
a chieftain as thou !" they shouted angrily, " and
if thou dost not get rid of that sly-faced wife of
thine, we will swear allegiance to him tomorrow."

Now if Maclean had been a strong man and
loyal to his wife, he would never have hearkened
to them, and by next morning many of them
would have been ashamed of their ugly thoughts,
for in their heart of hearts they knew Lady Elizabeth was both leal and true. But the great, sullen,

black-hearted man had grown weary of her gentle ways, and he was quite glad of an excuse to get rid of her.

So he told the chieftains they could do with her what they liked, so long as he heard nothing more of the matter.

And next morning he went away on a hunting expedition to the south of the island, saying that he would not be back for three or four days.

That same evening, as Elizabeth was sitting down by the rocks along with her baby boy and old Mairi the nurse, some of the chiefs who had met together in the cave came along, led by Lochtarish, and seized her, giving her no time even to kiss her son, and carried her off to a boat which was waiting nearby.

" But what do you want, and where are you taking me to ?" asked poor Elizabeth, as they flung her roughly into the boat and seated themselves beside her.

" 'Tis time for thee to bid farewell to all mortal things," replied Lochtarish gruffly, for the sight of her white face and frightened eyes tugged at his heart, which, long years ago, had been soft and kindly, like other men's. " We have no liking to be made mere vassals of the Campbells, and as long as thou art here, they will not be content without us. So we are taking thee to yonder island, where the next tide will free thee from all earthly ills."

In vain the terrified girl begged and entreated them to spare her life, and to row her over to Morven, whence she could go to her father's Castle. They only laughed at her. " Na, na ! we've had enough of thy father and thee," they cried, " not to speak of thy brother and thy lover. We'll do away with thee once and for all, then perchance there may be peace and security on Mull."

So they rowed to the island, which was but the flat top of a rock which was completely covered at high tide, and, throwing her on to it, they turned and rowed back in haste to Mull, without ever looking over their shoulders. Luckily, as it turned out, the tide was ebbing at the time, so Elizabeth had many hours in front of her before the water slowly rose to end her life.

But to the poor, doomed girl, as she paced up and down the rock, shivering with cold in the gathering darkness, it seemed as if it would have been kinder if the chieftains had thrown her out of the boat into deep water and let death come speedily and swiftly.

Meanwhile her brother Lorne and his friend had still been lingering in Morven hunting. And this night they were sleeping in a fisherman's hut down by the shore.

The fisherman himself was out with his boat, and

in the early hours of the morning he came into the little room where the two strangers were sleeping, taking off his wet clothes as he did so.

" What kind of morning is it ?" asked Lord Lorne, " and what promise is there of a good hunting day ?"

" It may clear later, my Lord," answered the man, " but now it is wet and misty, and the wind blows high. Had it not been for that, I would fain have rowed close up to the big rock yonder. For I thought I heard a cry, as of someone in distress, and I half thought I saw a flutter of something white. almost like a woman's skirt. But mayhap 'twas only a seagull screeching, or some poor beast, a dog or a cat, maybe, that has gotten on the rock in some way, and cannot get off again."

Lord Lorne started to his feet, a terrible dread filling his heart. Was it possible that red-bearded Maclean had heard of his visit to Duart Castle along with Malise Graeme, and in a fit of jealous fury had exposed his young wife on the rock ? It seemed unthinkable, yet something within him told him it was true.

" Here, my man !" he cried, " I will give thee ten merks if thou wilt go back with us to the island. I have a mind to see what the white thing is. With three of us at the oars we can make headway against any wind. Here, Graeme !" But Malise Graeme had been awake and listening, and he was already on his feet, his teeth clenched and his face quivering.

In five minutes the boat was speeding over the water, each man bending to his oars, and though no one spoke, the same question was rising in the minds of each : would they be in time ?

By God's mercy they were, but only just !

They found Elizabeth clinging to an iron stake which had been driven in the rock for fishermen to tie their boats to. The water was above her waist, and she was almost senseless; another quarter of an hour, and it would have been too late.

She was not aware of the friendly hands that lifted her into the boat, and wrapped her gently in the plaids that her rescuers had brought with them. It was not until she was safely in bed in the fisherman's hut, that she opened her eyes and gazed wildly round her.

"The water, the water," she moaned; "it is rising and rising every minute."

"'Deed is it," said the fisherman's kindly wife, who had risen from her own bed in order to give it to the half-drowned lady, and was now sitting beside her, chafing her frozen hands in her own rough, warm ones. "But this is no the rock, my lamb, and thou art safe on shore, and in thine own country, and among thine own clansmen. I'll bring my Lord of Lorne in, just for a minute, to look at thee and to assure thee that thou art safe; then thou wilt be a good bairn, and drink a sup of milk, and lie down and go to sleep again."

By the evening of the next day Elizabeth was back in her home at Inveraray, and everyone in the Castle, from MacCallum More himself down to the youngest scullery-maid, was so overjoyed at having their beloved young mistress once more among them, that anyone entering the Castle would have imagined that some great event, such as a wedding, was afoot.

The only thing that cast a shadow on the fair young mother's face was the thought of her child. But she knew that old Mairi would do her best for him. Sir Malise, whose eyes were sharpened by the love he still bore her, saw the shadow and divined its cause.

" Fear not for the bairn," he said, " for in two days I depart for England. At least so I have given everyone to believe. But where the Graeme hath gone once, he can go again, and peradventure he may pay a call on Mairi and her charge, ere he turn his horse's head towards the south."

The very next day a messenger arrived from Mull, bearing a letter from red-bearded Maclean to the Earl of Argyll. It contained the news of Elizabeth's death, and in it Maclean was brazen-faced enough

FRIENDLY HANDS LIFTED HER INTO THE BOAT

to say that his dearly loved wife had died in his arms, after every care and attention had been lavished on her, and that, to mark his respect and sorrow he had given her the most splendid and stately funeral that had ever been seen on the island. Moreover, he intended setting out himself for Inverary, attended by his kinsman, Maclean of Lochtarish, to let the Earl hear, from his own lips, the details of his daughter's illness.

" The base, slippery toad !" cried that nobleman, throwing the letter at his feet. " I wonder the words did not rise in his throat and choke him as he wrote them. But let him come ! Let him come ! A bonny surprise and greeting he will get here, I warrant him."

So the messenger was sent back to Duart Castle with fair words of invitation, while Malise Graeme chuckled and laughed, and Lord Lorne shut himself up in the armoury and began to sharpen his sword.

Next day the Englishman left the Castle, and it was noted that he took an extra horse with him, " in case," he said, " the one he rode fell lame." But if anyone had followed him, they would have found that he did not keep to the highroad, which would have taken him to Glasgow or the south, but branched off on a track that led him over the hills to Loch Linnhe and Morven.

Meanwhile Maclean and his companion arrived

at Inveraray, with downcast looks and a great appearance of woe, and they were taken by surprise when they found that instead of the Castle being plunged in mourning, everyone wore a particularly cheerful appearance. Argyll and his son met them in the great hall, and listened gravely enough to Maclean's account of the Lady Elizabeth's death and burial. But when he had finished his story, the Earl seemed to throw off his sadness with a little toss of his head.

" And so that was the way it happened," he said, " and I thank you, Maclean, for coming all this road to tell me about the bonny burial you gave her. I would fain have been there, but doubtless there was no time to summon me. I fear me you've not chosen the most suitable time to come with such news. For we're going to get a new mistress here, and I have assembled my chieftains this very night to hold a feast in her honour. Do you feel that you could bear to join us, or will you sup alone in your chamber ? "

" The wily old sinner," thought Maclean. " In spite of his loss he is taking to himself a new wife, and he fears that the sight of Lochtarish and myself will be as skeletons at the feast. But we have not come all the road from Mull to be put off with a bite in a room by ourselves."

So he replied that, sore at heart as he was, he and

his friend would like to join his host and his chieftains, and take a share in welcoming the new mistress to the Castle.

Though he knew that the Earl was a great man in the west, he was not prepared for the magnificence of the banquet which had been set out in the great hall; and when he saw the massive silver tankards and candlesticks, and the fine linen napkins, and the serving-men and the page boys, he felt that, perhaps, he had been foolish to part with a wife whose father could live in such a princely style.

But it was too late in the day for regrets, so, while his greedy eyes roamed round the room, watching the cooks bringing in all manner of dainty dishes, he stood at attention with the rest of the chieftains, watching for Argyll to bring in his bride.

At last the Earl appeared with a lady on his arm. She was tall and slender, and dressed in the most beautiful satin gown, embroidered all over with tiny pearls. On her head was a quaintly fashioned coronet of pearls, from which hung a white veil which entirely hid her face. The Lord of the Castle took his seat at the head of the table, placing the lady on his right hand. He gave a sign to Lord Lorne to sit down opposite him, with his two guests on either side. Then the chieftains took their places and the banquet proceeded, the lady only raising her veil sufficiently to enable her to eat.

When it was finished, Maclean, eager to please his host, sprang to his feet, and, raising his glass, asked everyone present to drink the health of the fair lady who had come to be mistress of the Castle. " If her face be as fair as her gown and her jewels," he added, " MacCallum More may well consider himself a happy man."

" Her face is fairer than any dress or any jewels," cried the Earl, and there was something in his tone that brought a cold fear to Maclean's heart ; " but in spite of her beauty those who should have been her nearest and dearest seem to have been unaware of it—aye, and unaware of the beauty of her soul— and they cast her out, therefore hath she come to Inveraray."

He made a little sign, and the lady threw back her veil ! A dead silence followed. The chieftains stood with their glasses raised, smiles of triumph on their lips, while Maclean and Lochtarish staggered back against their chairs, their faces white, their limbs shaking. For it was no bride of Argyll's that confronted them, but his only daughter, whom they believed to be lying under the waters of the Sound of Mull.

" This is the new mistress of Inveraray," said the Marquis, " so whom you buried with so great a fash at home, Maclean, ye ken best yoursel'. Ye needna trouble yoursel' to explain. All that matters to me is, that it was not my daughter. Now, aiblins, that you see her alive and well, ye'll drink her health wi' a lightsome heart." Shouting the slogan of the clan, the chieftains drained their glasses, but Maclean and his friend let theirs fall to the ground from their nerveless, hands, and without saying a word, turned to creep, like beaten hounds, from the hall.

But Lord Lorne was too quick for them. "By my troth," he cried, "but you're not going to escape thus easily. I have no wish to set the clansmen at each other's throats, for the quarrel is none of theirs. But thou and I must fight, Maclean, for our own honour, and our men can abide by the outcome."

So a deadly fight was fought on the Castle green between the brothers-in-law, and when it was over the Lord of Duart lay dead on the grass.

At the sight Lochtarish drew his sword and looked wildly round, expecting his turn to come next, but he did not know the spirit of the man with whom he had to deal.

"Thou canst go home," said Lord Lorne coldly; "either Maclean or I had to die, but there will be no more bloodshed over the matter. I am glad it is Maclean that hath fallen, for my sister is once more free, and there are those who love her better than did that great red-bearded lump."

Then, like the coward he was, knowing he was safe, Lochtarish raised his voice scornfully.

" Your sister may be free," he said, " but her son is not, and it is a poor mother that will leave her bairn to the fate that will befall young Roderick when I get back to Mull and tell this story."

" A fine job you'll have to find young Roderick on Mull, Lochtarish, for whatever fate you plan for him," said a mocking voice behind him, and, looking round, he was just in time to see Sir Malise Graeme place her son in Elizabeth's arms, while old Mairi scrambled down from the back of the second horse.

With a muttered curse the angry man turned and made his way to his boat, followed by the jeers of the Campbells, leaving the body of his Chief to be buried in alien soil and in a nameless grave.

As for Lady Elizabeth, everyone will know that she did not end her days at Inveraray. For it was not long before her faithful English lover turned his face in right earnest to the south, and he did not go alone.

VIII

THE TREASURES OF DUNVEGAN

I'M an old woman now, scarce able to hirple to the door on a summer's day, but perhaps I can tell you better than most folk the story of the treasures of Dunvegan, these precious heirlooms—the Horn, the Cup, and the Fairy Flag—that are kept in the great glass case on the wall of the old banqueting hall in the keep of Dunvegan Castle.

I have served in the Macleod family nearly all my life, I was nurse to the present Head of the Family, and when, as an infant he was carried down and shown, as is the custom, to the men of his clan, it was myself that carried him, and covered him with the Flag, and sang the fairy lullaby over him, while the clansmen drank his health from the Horn and the silver-mounted Cup, which were passed from hand to hand and from mouth to mouth.

I have my own little room up here in the Fairy Tower, with Jenny, my little grandniece, to wait on me, as if I were a lady born, and I often tell her stories about the treasures, for she never tires of hearing them. There is first the Horn, which takes us back to early days. For you must know that the

noble family which I serve is descended and takes
its name from Loid, the son of a King of Denmark,
so its members have the blood of fierce and gallant
vikings in their veins. This young man, so the
story goes, led a fleet of high-prowed boats round
the north of Scotland and conquered the Lews, and
instead of going home again, settled down, with
a wheen of his followers, on this island of Skye.

He married, and had sons and daughters, and one
of his descendants, Malcolm, who was Chief of the
Clan in his time, and who was possessed of by-
ordinar strength, brought to the Castle the Horn
of Dunvegan. And this was how he obtained it.

In these days herds of wild and untamed cattle
roamed about the country, living in the densely
tangled brushwood that covered so much of the
land, and doing great damage to the scanty crops
which the country folk managed to grow on the
poor, thin soil of their tiny crofts. These animals
were, as a rule, as frightened of the crofters as the
crofters were of them, and fled to their lairs when
they were attacked.

But in one of the deep mountain glens in the
island there was an enormous bull, with a massive
head and great spreading horns, which kept everyone in the vicinity in a state of terror. It was so
fierce and so strong that it trampled down everything that came in its way, and already it had

killed five men and seven dogs who had tried to
get near enough to it to stab it with their pikes or
pull it down and worry it as they would worry a
wild deer.

At last everyone became so terrified that they dared
hardly venture outside their huts, but sat inside in
gloom and darkness while the dreaded creature
ramped and roared about, trampling down the
growing crops, and playing havoc with the scanty
ricks of hay which had been stored up against
the coming winter. At last word was brought to
Dunvegan about this state of things, and when he
had heard the tale the Lord of the Castle started
to his feet. " Why was this kept from me ?" he
cried. " I am the father of my people, and God
hath given me great strength, and here am I, safe
in my Castle, while twenty miles away a brute
creature is killing my clansmen and laying waste
the glen, and no man hath told me of it."

So saying, he reached down his bonnet from the
wall, and strode out of his Castle, taking neither
breastplate nor shield, and with only his little
hunting-dirk stuck in his leather waist-belt. Some
of his gillies would fain have followed him, but,
added to his strength, he was mighty swift of foot,
and he strode up the hillside as one possessed.
Because of his pity for his poor retainers, and the
fierce fire of anger that burned in his heart at the

terror and loss which they had suffered, the twenty miles seemed as five, and the sun had not begun to sink ere he was pushing his way through the tangle of whin and bracken which grew in profusion on the edge of the ravine.

He paused for a moment ere he began to descend. It all looked so calm and peaceful : the bracken and the leaves of the birch trees turning to gold in the rays of the sun, the twitter of birds among the bushes, the cushat calling to its mate, the little heather-thatched huts nestling beside the burn far down at the bottom of the glen. Everything seemed just as usual, and it was difficult to believe that in this quiet spot men and women could only go about at the risk of their lives.

But, even as these thoughts passed through his head, the bushes to the right of him parted, and an enormous white bull stood before him, its head lowered and its eyes burning. It paused for a moment, pawing the earth with its hoofs, and tossing up turf in the air with its horns, bellowing in a strange, angry way meanwhile. Then with one great roar it rushed at the Laird, hoping to gore him with its horns, and then trample him to pulp under its heavy feet. But Malcolm Macleod was too quick for it. He sprang to one side, just in the nick of time, and as the great beast lurched forward, he seized a handful of its hair, and swung himself

up on its back, and there for a time he sat, his knees
well into its sides, each hand grasping a horn.
In vain the maddened creature rushed hither and
thither, it could not rid itself of its unaccustomed
burden, and when it tried to do so by rolling in the
brushwood, Malcolm took hold of the branches of
an overhanging fir tree and swung himself safely
up out of danger.

Again and again he returned to the fray, sometimes attacking the infuriated animal from behind
with his dirk, but because of the size of the weapon
he could only draw blood and nothing more;
sometimes meeting it face to face and trying,
by the sheer force of his strength, to thrust
it by its horns over the edge of the ravine;
sometimes merely dodging from bush to bush,
in the hope that it would weary itself out in its
mad pursuit.

At last, when he was wrestling with it, one of its
horns came off in his hand, and the animal, crippled
by the loss and maddened by the pain, came down
on its knees, butting wildly in its blind rage at the
stump of a tree. Quick as lightning, the young
chief seized his opportunity. Leaping astride the
angry brute, and bending low over its neck, he
plunged his dirk deep in its chest. The point
reached its heart, and, with one last resounding
bellow, that brought the cottagers to their doors in

frightened astonishment, it rolled over dead, a crumpled mass of unwieldy flesh.

Malcolm lifted his hunting-horn, and, putting it to his lips, blew a shrill, triumphant blast that brought the anxious country folk running up the sides of the glen. At the sight of their dead enemy, with their chief standing unhurt beside it, they shouted and danced as if they were fey, and the women knelt down and kissed the young Lord's feet, so thankful were they that the danger was removed, and that their bairns could play about once more in safety.

"The beast is yours," he said, "to do with what ye will. The flesh will feed you for a week, and as for the skin, you can tan it for brogues, or sell it to the first merchant who comes from the mainland. The only thing I care for is this Horn, which I will carry back with me to Dunvegan, to let those who come after me see what one of their forbears did with naught but his naked dirk and the strength of his own right arm."

So the Horn was carried to the Tower of Dunvegan and mounted, as you see, with a rim of solid silver, and it became the custom, when one chieftain died and his son stepped into his place, that the Horn should be filled to the brim with wine and presented to the new Head of the Clan, and that he should drain it at one draught, to show that he bade fair to be as strong and lusty a man as was his forbear Malcolm, the slayer of the wild bull of the glen.

*   *   *   *   *

That is the story of the Dunvegan Horn; now I must tell the story of the Dunvegan Cup.

In the days of Malcolm, he of whom I have been speaking, there were two brothers, Neil and Alisdair Glendubh, who rented between them a farm called Luskintyre in the island of Harris. This farm belonged to the Macleod. Now although Neil and Alisdair had to live together, they were bitter enemies, and each of them had his own flock of sheep and herd of cattle, and they were always on the outlook to see that the animals belonging to the one did not fare better than those belonging to the other. As timber was scarce in Harris, their fields were not fenced, so they had to hire men to watch their little patches of turnips and corn at night, in case the cattle should stray into them and destroy the crops.

One of the youths whom Alisdair Glendubh engaged was a lad named Lurran, whose mother lived in a cottage on the farm, and who really was not a mortal woman at all, but a witch.

She had been Alisdair's foster-mother, and a close affection existed between the two. The son, Lurran, had inherited some of her uncanny powers. He had the second sight and the power to see the Little Folk when they were invisible to other eyes, and he could run far more quickly than any other man or boy on the island.

One day, as he was watching Alisdair's corn, he saw a strange and unchancy sight. A grassy knowe which rose among the heather just in front of him opened, and by the light of the moon he saw hundreds of the Fairy Folk come out and dance on the greensward, tripping up and down in the most fantastic dances he had ever seen. None of his companions appeared to see anything, so he held his tongue and kept the discovery to himself. After they had danced for an hour, they formed in a body and came running across the meadow to where Alisdair's herd was grazing, and, forming a circle round one of the cattle, danced round and round it, singing a shrill little song meanwhile.

Lurran smiled to himself. "Ye canna bewitch Alisdair's cattle," he muttered; "my mother has seen to that. She has thrown her strongest spell over these beasts, so that the Fairy Folk have no more power to harm them than our old tom-cat at home. They may try what they can do with yon dark-coloured beasts o' Neil's; my mother left them unshielded, for she has little love for their master."

And, sure enough, the fairies left off trying to weave spells round Alisdair's steers, and tripped across to where Neil's bullocks were stretching their necks in the endeavour to obtain a mouthful of half-ripe corn. They formed their circle again, enclosing two of the cattle within it, and this time the spell worked, for as the fairies moved nearer and nearer the open knowe, from which a bright light issued, the animals went slowly along with them, and in a few minutes the whole eldritch company had vanished from sight with the booty they had taken.

Next morning, when the sun rose, the brown skins of two of Neil's cattle, with horns and hoofs attached, and filled with refuse, were found lying on the green knowe in the midst of the meadow, and loud were the threats and curses which came out of their owner's lips at the sight.

No one could solve the mystery, for the watchers had been on the watch, and the meadow had lain bathed in glorious moonlight all night. Besides, where had the flesh of the bullocks gone to ? That was the question on every man's lips, but no answer to it could be given. And everyone was more astonished and puzzled still, when the next night and the next again, in spite of constant watchfulness, two cattle from Neil Glendubh's herd disappeared, and in the morning their skins were found on the fairy knowe.

As he looked at the skins, and then at his brother's herd, out of which not one animal was missing,

Neil's heart was filled with hard and bitter thoughts, and his face grew sullen and lowering.

" 'Tis easy to ken what comes ower my bullocks," he cried. " They say we maun a' pay teinds to the Evil One, an' Alisdair pays his ain teinds an' mine out o' my herd."

Meanwhile a plan for a wonderful adventure was taking shape in Lurran's mind. He would follow the fairies into their fairy hill, and keep his eyes open to see what went on there.

So one evening he tiptoed softly in behind them, and sat down unobserved, close to the entrance. He found himself in a huge hall, carpeted with green and roofed with azure, while the walls were hung round with numberless mirrors, which reflected the light of ten thousand candles.   Down the centre of it ran two enormous tables, round which the Little Folk seated themselves and feasted on huge sirloins of beef, cut from the flesh of the animals over which they had thrown their spells.   Lurran drew his whinger and ate with the rest, but his heart stood still when, after the meal was done, a great wooden Cup was handed round, from which everyone present was expected to drink.   The Cup was of curious shape.   It had six sides, and the rim and the four legs on which it stood were of solid silver, curiously wrought.

As it came near his turn to drink, Lurran's hair

nearly rose from his head in dismay and perplexity.
For he knew that no mortal man could partake of
fairy wine and live. There was only one thing
that he could do. The entrance to the knowe was
not quite closed, so, when the Cup was handed to
him, and all the fairies looked at him with triumph
in their eyes, expecting to see him taste their wine
and fall dead at their feet, he dashed its contents on
the ground, and, grasping it firmly in his arms,
dashed through the narrow entrance, and made for
his mother's cottage with all the speed he could.

With shouts of rage, the Little Folk rushed after
him, pell-mell, up hill and down dale, but he soon
outran them, and, crossing a burn, put himself
out of all danger, for the Fairy Folk cannot cross
running water.

Breathless, he arrived at home, and told his
mother the whole story. " I'll soon protect ye from
their vengeance," she said, " if ye will but be contented to bide on this side the burn, and not to stray
far from the house." And she went out and threw
a spell all round the cottage, so that no fairy could
come near it.

So Lurran was safe for a time. But he grew tired
of hanging about the door of his mother's cottage,
and one evening he crossed the burn and went for
a long walk, and the fairies saw him, and set on him
in their hundreds and killed him.

When the news was brought to his mother that his body had been found lying on a mossy bank among the trees, and that no one knew how he had met his death, she just nodded her head and gave a queer little laugh.

" I know," she said, " 'twas all because of that Silver Cup standing yonder on the dresser," and she took the tankard and thrust it into the hands of her foster-son.   " Take it, Alisdair Glendubh," she cried, " for it was in thy service he got it, and I have no wish to cast eyes on it again."

So Alisdair carried it away to the farmhouse of Luskintyre.   But it did not stay there long.   For the quarrel between the two brothers grew more and more bitter, till at last Neil rose one night and killed Alisdair as he lay asleep, and pretended to all the world that his brother had choked himself with a bit of meat.

But the old witch knew better, for, like Lurran, she had the gift of second sight, and she had seen what had taken place in Alisdair's bedroom.

So she locked her cottage door one night at midnight, and flew over the sea on a broomstick to Dunvegan Castle.

Early in the morning she asked to speak with Malcolm Macleod, and she told him the whole story, and was back in her cottage ere the dew was off the grass.

Macleod, being a just man, determined that such a crime should not go unpunished. So he called together half a dozen of his men and took boat to Harris, and, going straight to the farmhouse of Luskintyre, he seized Neil Glendubh and hanged him on the nearest tree. Most of his possessions he handed over to the old witch to comfort her for the loss of her son and to reward her for the part she had played. But he carried the Magic Cup back to Dunvegan with him, and there it has remained ever since.

*   *   *   *   *

Then there is the Fairy Flag, fashioned out of nut-brown silk, with its cross in the centre and its magic elf-spots, wrought by fairy hands in strands of gold. How the creatures came to embroider the Holy Sign on it is mair than I ken, but there it is, and doubtless without it the Flag would not have its wondrous power.

It came langsyne into the hands of a younger son of the Macleod when he was away in the East, fighting in the Crusades. He was a valiant soldier, and so much thought of that his commander once sent him away alone on a secret errand across the desert. He had food and water with him, and for two days he rode on and on, with nothing for the eye to rest on but dry, burning sand. At last he came in sight of a mighty river, and his heart rose high, for he knew that his journey was wellnigh done, for on the other side of the river lay the palace of the king to whom he was sent.

But, as he approached it, an ugly old witch rose out of the sand. She was but a little body at first, with a wrinkled face and eyes like fire. But she waxed taller and taller, until at last she was so big and strong that she barred the way for the horse and its rider.

Sir Torquil Macleod drew his sword, but she was his equal, and drew her wand, which was about as thick as the handle of a broom, and together they battled and fought, and often it seemed as if the witch would have the best of it. Once she got so near that she got hold of his bridle rein, and was fain to scratch his eyes out with her nails, which were like claws; but he managed to get clear, and with one sweep of his sword he cut off her head.

Now, although he was such a gallant soldier, Torquil was a kindly man. So he got off his horse, and buried the poor old body deep in the sand; then he rode on.

When he came to the river he saw a ford, and, as he was riding through it, who should appear to him but the bonniest little fairy he had ever seen.

She was dancing in the sun on the surface of the water, and her dress was made of the loveliest rainbow hues. She had a star in her hair and a silver wand in her hand, and on her feet were little golden shoon.

" I bring thee a greeting from all the water-nymphs and fairies, Sir Knight," she said, " and a present as well. For that old hag whom thou hast slain was our deadly foe, and now we can roam among the rushes on the banks of the stream without fear. 'Tis good to come to dry earth at times when the moon is full and the stars look twinkling down. And as long as that old witch was alive we only left the river at the risk of our lives."

So saying she rose in the air and settled on his horse's mane, and presented him with a box of cedar wood. " Take that home with thee," she said, " as a token of gratitude from the Fairy Folk. In it thou wilt find a number of boxes, each smaller than the other, and in the smallest thou wilt find a magic banner, which, when thou art in danger, if thou wave it, will summon to thine aid a host of armed men. But thou must let a year and a day pass by ere thou puttest it to the test. Farewell," and she vanished.

Torquil Macleod fulfilled his errand safely, and not very long afterwards the Crusade ended, and he returned home. As soon as he set foot in Skye he wended his way to Dunvegan, and gave the box into the hands of his chieftain's wife, telling her how the Flag was to be used. She was a poor, silly thing with more than her fair share of curiosity, and she nearly lost the Flag to the clan by taking it out of its box as soon as Torquil's back was turned, and giving it a wee bit shake. I can tell you she was terrified when a big, bearded man in full armour appeared from nowhere, as it were, and, with an awful look on his face, held out his hand for the Flag.

Luckily her husband came in at that moment, having met Torquil on the road, and snatched the Flag away from her, and put it back in its box in a hurry, and locked the whole thing away in the great iron kist that used to stand in the great hall. And as he did so, the man disappeared. It was many a long day before it was taken out again, and that was when the Macleods went to fight with the Campbells, the last named being a great and mighty clan.

But the Flag was carried in front of our men, and lo and behold! our numbers were doubled; and the strange thing was that the men who joined our forces were not strangers, but their faces were kenned faces, and they wore the Macleod tartan. 'Twas said that they were clansmen who had fallen in the battles of former years.

Be that as it may, the Macleods were the victors, and over and over again this happened, till no one dare rise against them for fear of the Fairy Flag.

Times are quiet now, and swords rust in their scabbards, and the Flag has been ta'en from its kist and hung in the case beside the Horn and the Cup. But, to this day, when an heir is born in Dunvegan he is wrapped in the Fairy ·Flag, in token that he is put under its protection and that, if need be, he may claim its help whenever he is in danger in days to come.

IX

ESCAPE OF LORD OGILVIE

" THE news has come, Mother, and it is as we
thought. The death sentence is for all of them,
to be carried out at the Market Cross of St. Andrews,
on Tuesday next. And this is Friday night; they
have not left us much time. Uncle Patrick sent
the word by one of his servants, who is waiting
to ride back to St. Andrews, if we can supply him
with a fresh horse. I gave orders that Red Rowan
should be saddled, and that the messenger should
be given a good supper before he departs. Red
Rowan is slow, but he is not easily tired, and it
is more than likely that Uncle Patrick will send
the servant back on him with another message
tomorrow."

The speaker, Lady Margaret Ogilvie, held out
the letter which contained the fatal news to her
mother, the Countess of Airlie, and then sat down
beside her sister-in-law, Lady Helen Ogilvie, and
took her hand in hers in mute sympathy. For
Lord Ogilvie, like his father and all the members
of his House, had ever been an ardent Royalist,
and had recently fought under his cousin the

Marquis of Montrose, at Philiphaugh, on behalf
of King Charles. Everyone knows the result of
that ill-fated battle : how the army of the Covenanters, under General Leslie, inflicted a crushing
defeat on the Royalist party, whose forces were
completely routed, many distinguished officers and
noblemen being captured and, after a couple of
months' imprisonment and a very hurried trial,
sentenced to death.

Lord Ogilvie was one of these, and although his
father, the Earl of Airlie, had hastily retired to the
Highlands on hearing of his son's imprisonment
in St. Andrews Castle, in the hope of raising
a sufficient force to invade Fife and try to effect
a rescue, the message which had now been brought
to Cortachy Castle, the Forfarshire seat of the
family, showed that even if the Earl were successful
in his plans he would be too late.

But the women of the " Bonnie Hoose o' Airlie "
were as brave and far-seeing as the men, and in the
anxious days of waiting they had laid their plans,
and decided what *they* would do, if the safety of
their son, husband, and brother had to depend on
them alone. So the fatal news that had just arrived
found them neither unprepared nor unnerved.

" See to it that the rider be not allowed to depart
ere he receives my letter," said the Countess, a tall,
dignified woman in the prime of life. " I shall

write to my brother Patrick at once, craving for leave for all three of us to take a last adieu of James on Monday night—that is, the night before he is to suffer. Patrick being a Hamilton, and in favour, tho' I am loath to say it, with the Lords of the Covenant, will doubtless be able to manage that. I shall tell him to let us know for certain by Sunday night. And, Helen, write a wee bit line to your husband; 'tis but natural for you to do so. Patrick will see that it is delivered. Write nothing in it but what can be safely seen by all eyes. You might say that we hope to come, if we can get permission, and that we are feared that he will have taken to his bed with the shock, but that we trust that he will get strength from above to enable him to die like an Ogilvie. James is no fool; I think he will take the hint that we expect him to be in his bed. He may not understand the why and the wherefore, but he knows that this is not the first time that the women of his House have had to use their own wits and act for themselves in an emergency. He knows how you and me, Margaret, his mother and his sister held the Castle for two days and a night against the soldiers of the Commonwealth, and only yielded up the keys in order to save needless loss of life. And he knows how Helen there, the wife that he wedded when he was but a laddie of eighteen and she a lass of two years younger, stood

up to the great Argyll himself on his behalf, and
appeared before the Parliament at Perth in person,
and pled for his release, when he was confined in
the Tollbooth, what time the City o' Edinburgh
was visited by the Plague, and he was like to be
starved to death, because folk had all fled outwith
the walls. Na, na ; James will ken full well that we
will not let his head fall if we can help it, and
doubtless he will be quick to act on any little hint
we can send him as to how to behave in order to
work along with us."

With these words the strong-minded Countess
opened her desk, and, without wasting time on
further speech, began to write to her brothers ; and
her daughter-in-law, heartened and encouraged by
the composure of the older woman, lit the candles
which stood on the table in the oriel window, and
sat down to pen what might well be her last
message to her husband. When the letters were
sealed and dispatched, Lady Airlie would allow
no time to be spent in needless discussion and
lamentation.

" Our beds are the best places for us now," she
said, " and I lay it as a duty on you both to try to
sleep. It is near midnight, and we have done all
that we can do tonight. Tomorrow and Sunday
we can plan, and on Monday we can act, and we
will need all our strength and our judgment then.

SCOTTISH KEEPS AND CASTLES

148

Tonight we must just leave it in the hands of the Almighty, and pray that He will give my brother Patrick sense to carry out my instructions without trying to better them."

It was late afternoon on the following Monday, and a bitter wind swept over the little cathedral city of St. Andrews, freezing the water in the gutters, and causing the citizens to shiver with cold as they stood in little groups at the corners of the streets, and to draw their cloaks and mufflers closer round them. In spite of the cold, however, the town was buzzing with excitement, for were not five noblemen and gentlemen—to wit, Lord Ogilvie, the Earl of Hartfell, Sir William Spottiswood, Mr. William Murray, and Mr. Andrew Guthrie—to be executed by the Maiden at the Mercat Cross on the morrow, for the part they had taken in the conflict between the Royalists and the Covenanters at the battle of Philiphaugh.

Public feeling ran high. The majority of the citizens held that the sentence was a just one, and that, if the country were ever to be quiet, these risings must be put down. Others, and they were not a small minority, who still favoured the Bishops, and did not take kindly to the stern and gloomy religion of the extreme Reformers, shook their heads, and, while not venturing openly to advocate a free pardon, expressed their opinion that a term of imprisonment was all that was required, and that that sentence would have satisfied justice and spared the lives of five good, if mistaken, men.

Meanwhile, in a cell in the massive fortress, which, along with the ancient Cathedral, dominated the quaint little town, one of the condemned men lay in bed in sullen silence, his nightcap drawn so far down over his head that it covered his eyes, his face turned to the wall.

His jailer, a kind-hearted and talkative soul, had tried during the last two days to take his thoughts off his impending fate by bringing him a few dainties in addition to the ordinary prison fare, and by telling him stories of other prisoners, and all the bits of gossip he could think of.   It was all in vain.   Lord Ogilvie simply " picked at his meat," as the jailer expressed it, and turned a deaf ear and a melancholy and morose countenance to his would-be entertainer.   In fact, for the whole of the last day he had hardly eaten at all, and had lain with his face hidden, as though he were asleep, the jailor sitting for the most part beside him.

The worthy fellow, disappointed that his well-meaning attempts at conversation had met with such small success, rose from his seat at last, and with a grunt of disgust left the cell, and, locking the door securely behind him and hanging the key for safety on his girdle, went to join some of his companions before the blazing fire in the guard room.

Other soldiers who were in charge of some of the other condemned men were there before him, discussing with morbid interest the manner in which their special charges were bracing themselves to meet death on the morrow.

Everyone had a tale to tell more brave than the other, all except our friend, John Fletcher, who guarded Lord Ogilvie. " I am fair ashamed o' him," he said, " for when he was first brought here he was as brave and sprightly a gentleman as ever I saw. He is little and slight, but he showed a braver and more lightsome spirit than many a man twice his size. Even after he was sentenced he never faltered, and I bethought me that he would make a fine show on the scaffold. But on Saturday afternoon a letter was brought to him from his wife, by order of Sir Patrick Hamilton, and that did the mischief. There was nothing in it that I could see, for I took the liberty of reading it, as was my due. To my mind it was somewhat cold and distant—not the letter that a wife would write to a husband who was to die in two days.

" He sat and pondered over it for a good half-hour, turning it over and over in his hand. Then he seemed to grow tired all of a moment—perhaps he expected more soft words and lamentations in it—for he said suddenly that he would go to bed, and there he has lain ever since, getting more and more sullen and tongue-tied as the hours go on. A plague on him! He has no more spirit than a mouse, yet men have spoken of him as a brave and dashing soldier. His womenfolk are coming to bid him farewell tonight. His mother is a sister of Sir Patrick Hamilton's, and it's his interest that has gained them admittance. If their presence does not put some spunk into him he will have much ado to bear himself with dignity when he comes to meet the Maiden. 'Tis said he will be the first to suffer."

" I hate these partings and farewells," said one of the other guards, kicking a log farther on to the fire with the toe of his great jackboot. " 'Twere better to my mind to refuse admittance to the relatives, especially if they be, as they mostly are, of the womankind. 'Tis naught but tears and cries and useless bewailings, enough to shake the nerves of the strongest man."

" Nay, but if thou wert a married man thou wouldst think otherwise," remarked a third, and so the conversation drifted off into other channels.

Meanwhile dusk was falling, and in the cold dreariness of the January afternoon a party of six riders, three of them women, the others responsible-looking grooms, were cantering briskly over the wind-swept moorland that reached almost to the gates of St. Andrews. At the West Bow the ladies dismounted, and, throwing their bridles to the men-servants, passed quietly and without notice through the crowded streets in the direction of the Castle.

Meanwhile the serving-men led the horses to a quiet little hostelry near the West Gate, where there were few loiterers to notice them, and where, to judge from their welcome, they were well known. The horses were taken instantly to the stables and rubbed down, and if any curious onlooker had been present, he might have noticed that two of the animals received special care, their joints being well rubbed, their shoes inspected, and a double supply of oats put in their manger.

The ladies on their way to the Castle had to pass the Mercat Cross in the public square, and as they did so one of them staggered for a moment, as if she had been seized with sudden illness, for there on a platform in front of it stood the Maiden, that newfangled instrument of excution, ready for its dreadful task next day. It was Lady Helen Ogilvie, walking between her mother-in-law and her sister-in-law, and, brave as she was, the sight of the hideous machine seemed to bring before her with awful clearness the danger in which her husband stood.

"Hold up, Helen, and do not give people cause to notice you," said Lady Airlie in a low voice, and yet so sharply that the young wife drew herself up and walked proudly on. "Keep yourself easy, lassie," she whispered more gently, when they had passed through the crowd and were walking quietly towards the Castle gates. "Remember that, if all goes well—and with God's help I do not see why it shouldna—James should be far on his road to Blair-Atholl and safety, ere that machine is set to work tomorrow at noon. They dare hardly take the head off a woman for an adventure of that sort, else would I tremble for Margaret's."

"Oh, I think that will be safe enough ; I'll make love to the Lords of the Covenant," replied her daughter, who, blessed with an irrepressible spirit, was always most cheerful when the danger was greatest.

Arrived at the great iron-studded gate the three dauntless women drew their hoods closer over their faces, as if to hide their grief from the curious eyes of the guards, and, ringing the great clanging bell, stated their errand, and, asked to be taken to Lord Ogilvie's cell. The request met with a ready answer—Sir Patrick Hamilton had seen to that—and without waste of time they were led by the flickering light of torches along the echoing stone passages till they reached the small room where the prisoner was.

He looked up languidly as they entered, and at
the sight of him all three ladies burst into a volume
of most distressing sobs, Lady Ogilvie flinging herself
in a passion of grief across his bed. The guards,
with real sympathy and kindness of heart withdrew
into the corridor, saying that they would return at
eight o'clock, two hours being the time allowed
for such leavetakings. No sooner had they closed
the door, leaving the cell in semi-darkness—for it
was only lit by a couple of candles—than a strange
upheaval took place. "Quick, Jimmie," whispered
Lady Margaret, and in a moment the prisoner was
out of bed, the dismal look gone, his face wreathed
in smiles.

"I kenned ye wouldna fail me," he replied
below his breath, rapidly donning his sister's dress,
redingote, and hood in one corner, while she as
rapidly put on nightshirt and nightcap in another—
then, jumping into bed, drew the blankets up to
her chin, while Lady Airlie and Lady Ogilvie kept
up such a succession of broken sentences and sobs
as might be expected under the circumstances.

"Keep it up, Mother," he went on, "and, Helen,
lie across Margaret's legs just as you were lying
across mine. If anybody comes in, turn your face
to the wall, Margaret, and draw the pirnie well
down over your een. When I read the letter I
minded how we used to play at escaping from prison

when we were bairns together at Cortachy. And
I minded how our plan was ever to change into one
another's clothes. We were so like one another
then—as for a mercy we are like one another now—
that when we wore each other's things nobody, not
even mother here, knew the difference. So when
I got Helen's letter, and heard you were all coming,
I thought there might be such a plan, and I turned
it over and over in my mind, till light broke through.
I saw you expected me to be in my bed, so to bed
I went. And I made it as easy for Margaret as
I could, by pulling the pirnie down and the bedclothes up, and keeping my face to the wall. Faix !
but I was near suffocated. I havena spoken much
either, so your best plan is to be silent also. 'Tis
to be expected of a man who is to die tomorrow.
And if the rest of us get out safely, 'twill be tomorrow
morning ere they discover the trick that has been
played. Eh ! but I would like to see Argyll's face
when the news is brought to him that I have escaped,
and that there is nobody for him to wreak his wrath
upon but Margaret there !" And Lord Ogilvie, in
spite of the awful danger which hung over his head,
gathered his sister's cloak round him and shook
with laughter.

"'Tis time to laugh when the Grampians are
betwixt you and St. Andrews," said Lady Airlie
severely, for she was afraid that even the sound of

his wife's long-drawn-out and hysterical sobs would
not cover what was, after all, a fairly cheerful conversation. As she well knew, it was hard to be
gloomy in her son James's company, no matter
in what danger he stood. As for poor Lady
Helen, lying face downwards across her sister-
in-law's bed, her sobs were real enough, and all
the more serviceable because they were the outcome
of suppressed anxiety, excitement, and fear.

So the two long hours dragged themselves away,
and when the guards once more opened the doors
of the cell, and announced in sympathetic tones
that the moment for parting had come, they found
three grief-stricken women, handkerchiefs to their
eyes, standing round the bed, who, in mournful
silence, broken only by stifled weeping, kissed the
prisoner one by one and slowly turned to the door.

As they did so, the figure in the bed turned its
face to the wall, and, with a heavy sigh, drew the
bedclothes up round its head.

The guards, tho' to all appearance but rough,
war-hardened men, had nevertheless a soft spot in
their hearts, so they forbore to talk to the distressed
women who, their hoods drawn round their faces,
stumbled along the dark corridors, which, as we
have said, were lit only by the flickering light of
two torches, carried by the soldiers.

Indeed, a sigh of relief came from John Fletcher,

as he ushered them out into the cold darkness of
the streets and bolted and barred the door behind
them.

"That is one job weel by," he cried, "for I hate
the leavetaking waur than the scaffold. That is
soon over, but it takes lang years ere the women
forget. Now I maun gang and see if I canna
persuade his Lordship to take some meat, just to
strengthen him for the morrow."

But his well-meaning attempts met with small
success. In spite of all his coaxing, the prisoner
neither spoke nor moved, and at last he set down
the tray beside the bed, and, with a brief "Good-
e'en to you," turned the key in the door and left,
as he imagined, the doomed man to his own
thoughts.

Meanwhile the three conspirators had rapidly
traversed the town, now quiet and almost deserted,
for there had been a heavy fall of snow which had
driven the citizens to the comfort of their
own firesides.

At the city gates no one paid any special heed to
them, except to wish them a safe walk home on such
a wintry night, for they were taken for country-
women from the neighbouring hamlet of Crail.
But once out of sight of the gates they turned
inland, and soon reached a little wood, out of which,
at a low hoot from Lady Ogilvie, which might

have been taken for the cry of an owl, came one of the grooms, leading two horses.

There was a bundle tied to one of the saddles, which Lord Ogilvie seized, and with it in his arms dropped down into a ditch. In less time than it takes to tell he was on the road again, no longer in woman's clothes, but in breeches and doublet, the light of the scarcely rising moon glimmering faintly on dagger and pistol.

" Ye'll find Margaret's fal-lals in the ditch," he said lightly, " and I'll give your love to my father. He'll be a proud man, I can tell you, when he thinks of his womenfolk." And with that he leaped into the saddle and was gone, honest John Wilson, his foster - brother and boyhood's friend, galloping neck by neck beside him.

It was not for nothing that the faithful groom had spent his time for the last three days, ever since the fateful message had been brought to Cortachy Castle, in attending to those two horses, on whose endurance and fleetness of foot the life of his dearly loved master depended.

They repaid him now for his efforts, for they never drew breath nor faltered till they had traversed the counties of Fife and Kinross, and pressing down the Ochil Pass, arrived next morning, with staggering limbs and white with foam, in the Vale of Menteith, having carried their riders into comparative safety.

Two days later they bore them triumphantly into the Royalist camp at Blair-Atholl, where the Earl of Airlie, having succeeded in raising an army, but, as he thought, too late to save his son, was waiting, with a sad and heavy heart, to hear of his death on the scaffold.

But we are running on too far ahead in our story, and must go back to the Castle at St. Andrews, and see how brave Lady Margaret fared after John Fletcher turned the key in the lock and left her alone in her cell. At first she lay breathless with anxiety, straining her ears to hear any sound that might tell her that the trick had been discovered, and that her brother had been recaptured and was being brought back. But no one came near her, and all seemed quiet in the prison. So as hour after hour passed by—nine, ten, eleven, midnight; she heard the great clock on the tower ring them all— she began to breathe more freely, certain that Lord Ogilvie had got safely away, and would be by now many miles from the city.

By two o'clock she came to the conclusion that she could allow herself a little sleep, and when she awoke in the gray, glimmering dawn her heart was light, and she could quite enjoy the thought of the surprise that was awaiting the Lords of the Covenant.

It was on John Fletcher that the first shock fell.

When that worthy man unlocked the door and entered the tiny apartment, a lantern in one hand, a tray in the other, his face drawn out with a solemnity befitting the occasion, he nearly dropped to the ground with horror and dismay.

For there in the bed, instead of a motionless and despairing man, he saw, sitting well up against her pillows, a very good-looking young woman, whose long, chestnut-coloured hair, crowned by the pirnie, was hanging round her shoulders, and whose likeness to Lord Ogilvie left him in little doubt as to what had happened, and how the trick had been played which had allowed the latter to escape.

She greeted him with a cheery smile. " Come away in, my man," she said, " for I'm uncommon glad to see you. It was a real hardship for me not to eat my supper last night, but I thought it was safer to abstain. I might have spoken and betrayed myself. So I am ready for a right good breakfast. And dinna fash your head about the consequences of this. I will take them all on my own. Just send a message to my Lord of Argyll to tell him that by God's mercy the bird hath escaped out of his cruel and deceitful hands, and another to my mother— doubtless you will find her in my uncle Sir Patrick Hamilton's house—asking her to send me some clothing, for I have no wish to bide in this hard bed longer than I need."

" But, madam," stammered the jailer, looking round the bare cell, as if he expected his late prisoner to be hidden in some crevice of the wall, " where is Lord Ogilvie, and do ye ken what the law says about aiders and abetters of an escape ?"

" Where Lord Ogilvie is at the present moment, I just cannot say," replied Lady Margaret calmly ; " but, as he is a sensible man, I expect he is far from St. Andrews by this time. As for the law about aiders and abetters, I hardly think that when the story gets about the Lords of the Covenant, even one so bitter as Argyll himself, will dare to wreak their vengeance on a woman. Their own wives and sisters would have done the same, and in their heart of hearts they know it."

Her words proved true. Angry as he was about the escape of his enemy, the Marquis of Argyll could not carry out his desire for retaliation in the face of the sympathy and admiration expressed by most people, even those who differed from her family in politics, for Lady Margaret's brave act. So, after two' days imprisonment, she was set at liberty, and allowed to accompany her mother and sister-in-law home to Cortachy Castle, where, we may be sure, they received a royal welcome from their kinsfolk and acquaintance.

X

A WOMAN'S STRATEGY

I AM an old woman now, and only fit to sit at the fireside and mind the bairns, while my good-daughter goes out to work among the beasts in winter, or to help with the turnips and the hay and the harvest in summer, and so earn enough to keep herself and me and the two little laddies ; for it is a twelvemonth past, come Martinmas, since my only son, Wat, lay down with a fever and died.

But while my fingers are busy with my knitting, and the bairns have lain down for a sleep in the big box bed, and all is quiet about me, my mind goes back to the days when I was young and active, and thought as little of a hard day's work, as I think now of the trouble of going out to the well, which after all is only a stone's-throw from the door, and filling the kettle, and coming in and making up the fire, so as to have a cheery low and something hot ready for Jeannie when she comes in, often wet and weary, from her work outbye.

I was the hired lassie at the Manse of Kinneff in those days, and a right good place I had, for the minister and his wife, Mr. and Mrs. Grainger, had no bairns, and tho' my mistress was strict enough in the way of seeing that I did my work, both the master and she treated me more like one of their own than a stranger, which was very heartening, seeing that I had a stepmother at home who was none too kind.

Especially does my mind dwell on the share I had —only a very little one, it's true—in the great work of upholding the honour of this auld land of ours, by preventing the Southron loons carrying its Crown and Sceptre and the Great Sword of State— which have ever been counted the sacred signs of sovereignty—away to London, and so making our ancient realm just an outlying bit of England, without either King or Crown to show that it still is a kingdom distinct by itself, with its ain rights and privileges.

It was in the year 1651, and I'd just turned nineteen, when, one clear September day, as I was washing up the dinner dishes at the kitchen door, the mistress came out to me with her hat on.

"Haste thee, Alison," said she. "The minister has gone to Stainhive for a meeting and will stay the night at the manse, and it is sic.a bonny afternoon I think you and I will e'en have a ploy on our own account. You know how lonesome and dowie Mrs. Ogilvie is feeling, shut up as she is in that great barn of a Castle at Dunnottar, neither allowed to go in nor out, tho' daresay she would need to come out before she goes in. The only strangers who are allowed to enter the Castle are, as you know, you and me, and that because of my ancient friendship with Margaret Ogilvie. For she and I were cronies when we lived in Edinburgh for our schooling, and the friendship has lasted ever since.

"The English general has sense enough to know that a delicately reared lady like the Lady of Barras might pine and fade in that great gloomy fortress if she had never a woman body to speak to save that sour-faced waiting-maid of hers, who, rumour says, is in the General's employ as a spy. So we'll just make the most of our privileges, and hie away to Dunnottar. I want to take some hards of lint with us, I promised Margaret I would bring her some. She has her wheel with her at the Castle, and if she has the lint, she can always wile away an hour spinning. So while I put on my redingote and tie up the bundle, do thou saddle Donald and dress thyself seemly, but not too fine. For we have to find our way through the English camp, and you are too young and bonny to risk drawing the notice of the Southron lads, who are none too civil to Scottish maidens."

"'Deed, mem, you are both young and bonny yourself!" I cried, laughing, as I dried my last plate, and ran up to the stable to saddle and bridle

old Donald and put him on the pillar-chains, till
I had gone up to my loft in the manse to don my
new wincey skirt and the plaid shawl which my
father had bought for me at St. Modan's Fair.

And what I said was true. For my mistress at
this time was only six-and-thirty, twenty years
younger than the minister, and she was a comely
woman, and young for her years.

It was not long ere we were on the road, my
mistress mounted on Donald, with three great
bundles, or hards, of lint strapped on his broad
back behind her, while I walked barefoot alongside,
my one pair of shoes tied together and hung round
my neck, so that I could put them on, along with
the thick knitted stockings rolled up inside them,
when we came within hail of Dunnottar.

That grim and mighty stronghold was a good
five miles from the manse, but we had it in view all
the time, for, as all the world knows, it is built on
a rock that stands right out in the sea, with a
deep cleuch between it and the mainland, which
situation makes it, by the grace of God, one of
the strongest fortresses in Scotland and almost
impossible to overthrow.

I say by the grace of God, for truly our ancient
realm had need of God's grace and protection in
those days. For the King had fled to France, and
the Protector, as they called him, Master Oliver

Cromwell, was trying to get himself set in his place, or so it seemed to me, and the country was plunged, from end to end, in strife and bloodshed.

The few folk in Scotland who did not want Master Cromwell and his " Commonwealth "— which was the form of government he had set up in England after the Puritans had beheaded our lawful King, Charles I.—still wished for a King, so we crowned his son, Charles II., at Scone.

The outcome of that was, that Cromwell marched with his followers to Scotland and defeated the Royalists, as they called the King's men, at Dunbar, and took all the Castles to the south of the Forth— Tantallon and Hume, Roslin and Borthwick, and, in the end, Edinburgh Castle itself.

Now when Scotland and England had been joined together, which befell in 1603, about thirty years before I was born, the King of Scotland, James VI., had gone away to live at Windsor, which doubtless was bigger and grander than Edinburgh Castle. He had taken all his belongings with him, for if all tales be true, he had no intention of coming back to our bare little northern land ; but he could not take his Crown, nor his Sceptre with which he touched the parchments on which new laws were written, nor his great Sword of State with which he made plain men into Knights and Earls. Doubtless he found finer things in London; but these belonged to Scotland, her Honours, as men called them, for they were the signs that our northern land was still a kingdom, even though she had had to take England as a friend and partner.

So if the Honours of Scotland had been guarded before, they were better guarded now, and it has always seemed to me providential that there was a stronghold like Dunnottar to bring them to, when Cromwell marched on Edinburgh, after the battle of Dunbar.

But he and his Generals were determined to have them, not, so men said, because they were the Emblems of Royalty and therefore sacred, but because they were worth a mint of money, and hungry soldiers must be fed and foreign mercenaries paid.

So an English army had been brought up to Dunnottar, under a General called Lambert; and as it seemed that the Castle could not be taken by force of arms—as, indeed, how could it be?—this army had just sat down in front of it, allowing no communication with the mainland, thus hoping to starve the garrison into submission and so obtain possession of the prize.

On the day of which I am speaking we passed through the English lines without much trouble, save that some of the English lads threw such pretty words at me that I felt my cheeks redden, and my mistress bade me pull my shawl well up over my head, so that my face could not easily be seen.   When we came to the edge of the cleuch which separates the Castle from the mainland my mistress had to dismount and have Donald tethered to a post. Our hards of lint were examined here by a sentry, who opened out one of them and stuck his pike through the rest, in case we had anything hidden inside the soft, white, fluffy stuff.

Then, my mistress taking one bundle and I taking two, we struggled down the narrow, rocky path which led to the bottom of the ravine, and up the other side to where a little postern in the outer wall gave access to the beleaguered Castle. The sentry on the wall had seen us, and the coast being clear—for, to do them justice, the English were honourable foes—a little nail-studded door was opened a few inches, just enough to let us squeeze through with our bundles, and bolted and barred with marvellous speed behind us.

Once inside the postern, a few turnings and twistings brought us to the great hall, where a number of men-at-arms were busily engaged lifting some of the flat stones that formed the floor. Scullions and serving-men stood by, and among them I saw the harsh features and hideous head-

dress of Jean McIntosh, waiting-woman to Mistress
Ogilvie.

Ere I could lay down my bundles and cross to her
side, a sweet voice sounded from the gallery that
ran round the hall far above our heads, and which
was reached by a stone staircase hidden in the thick-
ness of the wall.

" Oh, Mary Grainger ! but you are a blessed
sight. And is that the lint that you promised to
bring ? Come up to my chamber and rest yourself,
and give me some news of the outer world. Jean
McIntosh, see and look after Alison, and have that
lint carried to the store-room till I have a mind to
spin."

I wondered that the lady did not run down, as
was her wont, to greet my mistress and lead her
upstairs with her own hand ; but when I was
summoned to her chamber a little later, to show
her how I oiled my wheel, for, young as I was,
I was counted a good spinstress, I saw traces of
tears on her cheek, and from the look on my
mistress's face, as she stood gazing in silence out
of the narrow window over the wide expanse of
glittering sea, which was all that could be seen from
the apartment, I knew that something untoward
had happened.

But neither of the ladies said anything, and after
I had put Mrs. Ogilvie's wheel to rights, and

12

showed her the proper way to handle her distaff, for she was but a beginner at the job, I descended to the great hall again, and sat down to the very frugal supper of a barley bannock and a morsel of salt herring, which Jean McIntosh had set out for me in a little recess at the foot of the stair. I noticed as I did so that the paving-stones had been replaced, and that Mr. Ogilvie, who was, as I have said, in command of the Castle, was standing before the fire, talking in a low and anxious tone with a group of grave and bearded men-at-arms.

It was plain that trouble of some kind was brewing, and Jean McIntosh was not long in enlightening me as to its nature.

" I'm sorry no to be able to gie ye butter on your bannock, or a drop o' milk to drink," she said, and there was a ring of satisfaction in her voice that made me feel as if I would like to slap her. " Our provisions here are running low: they have just been counting the barrels of herring and the bags o' meal that are left in the dungeon, and it's my opinion the master may as well deliver up the Castle soon as syne, for starvation is an ill neighbour, and starvation it will be very shortly."

" Oh, but, Jean! Mr. Ogilvie cannot give up the Castle," I replied aghast, for, knowing the strength of the fortress, such a termination of the siege had never entered my head. " If he did, the Honours

would fall into the hands of the English, and starvation would be better than that.   Besides"—and I
lowered my voice—"has not a letter been sent to
France, asking King Charles to help him by sending
a ship to take the Honours over the sea, so that they
may be out of danger.   Surely it will be coming
one of these nights—if it lay far out no one would
suspect, and a little boat could easily reach it.
Then, Mr. Ogilvie's work being done and the
Honours of Scotland safe, he could open the gates
and march out in the face of all the King's enemies."

   "An easy plan, gin it could be carried out," said
Jean scornfully, "but the letter has been away
this month and more—plenty of time for all the
ships in France to have been here.   A watch has
been kept on the tower every night sin syne, to look
for a glimmer of light out to sea—for so was it
planned—but never a glimmer has come.   Na, na ;
King Charles has forgotten us, say I, or else he
is powerless to help, and I, for one, would open the
gates the morn, and let the Englishmen take the
Crown and Sceptre away to London if they want.
No but what they would be disappointed with
them, for if all tales be true they are but poor stuff
compared with the Crown of England and all the
other jewels that came to King Jimmie when
Elizabeth of England died.

   "Oh, Jean !" I cried again, shocked at her want

of loyalty; but she just laughed at my horrified face, and before either of us could say more my mistress came down the stairs, and I had to put on my shawl in a hurry, for the nights were short, and we had a long way to go.

Donald was waiting for us where we had left him, and after the mistress had mounted we travelled in silence, till we had passed the English camp and were well on our road. I could see that she had something more than ordinary on her mind, so thought it was well not to disturb her with idle talk. At last she drew a long sigh, as if she were wakening out of a dream, and reaching down in the gloaming she put her hand on my shoulder.

"They are in sore straits in the Castle, Alison," she said, and in her voice was the least little bit of a tremble. "No help has come from France, and the provisions are running down. Someone must have got word of this to General Lambert; it seems as if there might be a traitor in the Castle, for the General has written to George Ogilvie asking him to surrender, and promising that no ill will befall either him or his household, if only the Honours are delivered up into English hands. Needless to say, Ogilvie has written back absolutely refusing to think of such a thing; but men cannot live without food, lassie, and the stores at the Castle are running very low. They may tighten their belts, and hold out for another fortnight or even three weeks—even Margaret can face that—but after that the end must come. That is, if you and me, with the help of the minister, cannot find a way out."

"You and me, mem!" I replied in astonishment. "What can a couple of women like us do?"

"I think we could do a lot, Alison," said my mistress bravely, "if we had plenty of courage and nerve, and trust in God. A plan has come into my head, and both the Governor and his wife think it might be carried out; but I must talk it over with the minister first, and for safety's sake, in case people question you, the less you know about it at present the better."

"But you will let me help?" I cried anxiously, my heart all a-jump at the thought of having a part in such a high emprise.

"Wheesht, lassie!" said Mrs. Grainger, looking round in alarm. "You do not know who may be on the road. When the time comes, I will be glad of your help, for I know you are both leal and true, but in the meantime say nothing. A rumour may be spread about the country in a day or two that Sir John Keith, youngest son of the Earl Marischal, to whom, you know, the Castle belongs, has managed to get the Honours to France by sea. If you hear that, you can agree with it. Say that somebody told you so, but you cannot vouch for the truth of it. Even so they will put two and two together, and think that you have heard it at the Castle—and believe it."

And sure enough, within the next week, persistent rumours began to get about that the Honours were gone, and that George Ogilvie was but waiting to hear of their safe arrival before he gave up Dunnottar. When anybody spoke to me about it, I answered as my mistress had bidden me, and smiled to myself meanwhile.

As for the mistress, her thoughts seemed to have left Dunnottar altogether, and settled on a fine pair of sheets that Jimmie Stiven, the village weaver, was weaving for a wedding present for her youngest sister, who was to be married in Edinburgh at Martinmas. She had spun the thread for these herself, and great and open were her lamentations when she discovered that all the thread of that special make was finished, and that any lint she still had in the house was blackened, and would spoil the sheets if it were used. I greatly wondered when I first heard her laying off her complaint to the elders' wives who chanced to be in the manse one day, as I knew there were three hards of bonny white lint lying up in the topmost garret; and I had just opened my mouth to tell her so when she shot me a warning glance and went on to explain that she had taken most of her good lint across to the

Lady at Dunnottar, and she saw nothing for it but to go and ask for some of it back again, so that she could spin more thread and the sheets be finished in time.

Then I understood.

The very next day the weather broke, and, instead of warmth and sunshine, there were lowering skies and a persistent drizzle of rain.

I was cleaning up the kitchen, just about midday, when the door opened and Mrs. Grainger came in.

" Alison," she said, " we'll away over to Dunnottar. Put a thick cloak on you, for we'll be wet before we get back."

" Go to Dunonttar !" I exclaimed in astonishment. " Had we not better wait for a drier day ?"

Then my mistress came a step nearer, and spoke in an undertone. " The time has come when I need your help, my bairn. And the rainy day makes the job easier. I sent a letter to Mrs. Ogilvie, telling her I was coming, and I did not forget to mention that I would need to bring home with me one of her hards of lint. I stated what it was for, also, to finish the pair of sheets for my sister's wedding present. So whichever Englishman passed the letter into the Castle knows the why and the wherefore of my visit."

Then my heart leaped to my mouth, and I saw it all. It was so simple, and yet so clever. But I saw one difficulty. " The Sword and the Sceptre may go into the lint," I whispered, but not the Crown —it is too big."

" Wheesht, lassie !" replied Mrs. Grainger, seizing me by the arm and looking round as if the kitchen walls might have ears. " I am going to put on my old plaited redingote," she added casually. "On a rainy day like this, who will notice how shabby and old-fashioned it is ? And under it there is plenty of room."

The minister came out to the doorway to see us depart, and I fancied that his lips were moving as he put his wife up on Donald, as if he were praying for our safety. But he bade us farewell cheerily enough, and stood and watched us till a turn of the road hid us from his sight. We did not speak much to one another during our five-mile journey ; our thoughts were set on the risks that lay before us—at least mine were. For if we were discovered, it might mean death or banishment, and at nineteen life is sweet, and one's own land is best. All the same, I would not have stood in the shoes of any other maiden on that wet and dreary afternoon, for all the gold in Christendom.

We had no difficulty in passing the sentries. Apparently my mistress's letter had aroused no suspicion, as privately, in my heart, I had feared it might. Indeed, one of the officers suggested, as we were tying up Donald, that he might send a lad across to help us to bring the lint back, as the path down the side of the cleuch was slippery, owing to the rain.

" It is real good of you to think of it," said my mistress calmly, " but there is no need to trouble you. I have my maid, Alison Wishart, here with me, and she is a strong, strapping lass, and can pick her steps over a muddy road like any deer."

So we were allowed to go on alone, to our great relief. It was with great relief also that we found that Jean McIntosh was ailing and in her bed, for we did not trust her, neither did Mrs. Ogilvie. She made a little grimace when my mistress asked where Jean was, and replied with a smile, " I thought this was one of the days when Jean was better out of the road, so I e'en slipped a drop or two of neat's-foot oil into her broth, and the poor body was so upset that she had to take to her bed, and she has never lifted her head since she lay down. Doubtless she'll feel better tomorrow, as so "—and her somewhat worn and weary face lit up—" if our plans do not miscarry, will we all."

We passed an anxious hour, pretending to laugh and talk as usual, and to relieve the strain I gave Mrs. Ogilvie a lesson in spinning, tho', to tell the truth, I doubt if one or other of us knew what we were doing. Then we made a pretence of eating what poor fare our host and hostess could set before us, and then the time came for us to depart.

The hard of lint had already been carried down from the store-room, and while Mrs. Ogilvie herself guarded the door, her husband brought the precious treasures, which he had sworn to guard with his life, out of their hiding-place in a secret niche in the wall and laid them on the table. Oh! but it was wonderful to see them. The glittering gold Crown all set with precious stones, with its pinnacles of gold, each finished with a pearl. And the slender silver Sceptre, with a bonny globe of crystal, as big as a hen's egg, on top of it. And the great Sword of State, in its purple and gold scabbard, which seemed too long to be hidden in one solitary hard of lint. It was me, I knew, who had to carry the lint, and I fancied every soldier in the camp would see the point of its scabbard sticking out at one end and its hilt at the other.

But Mr. Ogilvie bedded it skilfully in the soft, fluffy mass, with the Sceptre beside it, and teased and pulled out the lint, and wound it round with a bit of stuff torn from an old curtain, just allowing enough of the white fluff to show through the holes to let everyone see what it was I carried.

" That is as good as I can make it," he said at last. " You must keep it partly under your cloak, Alison, as if to shield it from the rain. And may the

Lord, in His mercy, prevent any soldier from running his pike through it!"

"Now for the Crown," he went on, and paused in perplexity. For the Crown was an awkward thing to hide, with its hoops and pinnacles.

But my mistress was ready for him. As I have said, she had donned an ancient redingote which had belonged to her grandmother, and which was so wide, and at the same time so closely plaited, that it stood out well from her waist. Lifting up the skirt, she showed the Governor how she had folded a shawl above her other skirts, in the folds of which hung a black linen bag, just big enough to hold the Crown.

"It is a simple plan," she said, "yet I think it will suffice. I am more afraid of Alison's burden than my own. If there is no suspicion of any sort they will not think of searching me, and my skirt is so full they will neither see the Crown when I walk nor when I am once settled on Donald's back. As for mounting, I must just manage that the best way I can."

"Now God shield you for brave women!" cried Mr. Ogilvie, as, the Crown safe in its hiding-place and the lint firmly grasped in my left arm, we parted from his wife, who kissed us with trembling lips. Without loss of time we made our way, attended by our host, through the great hall and slipping out of the postern, began to pick our steps down the muddy ravine.

" Methinks I hear the Crown rattling, Alison," whispered my mistress anxiously, as she slipped on a slab of rock.

" Nonsense, mem," I replied, for my courage was rising once I was out in the fresh air. " How can it rattle when it is wrapped in one of Mr. Ogilvie's finest kerchiefs? It was but a little stone which you loosened with your foot."

But my turn for fear came when, as we were ascending the path on the other side of the cleuch, I looked up and saw a tall figure talking to the sentry, close to where Donald was tethered. He was dressed differently from the ordinary soldiers, wearing a doublet and breeches of dark green cloth, with a soft buff-coloured hat and sleeveless coat, and long leather boots which reached to his thighs. From his right shoulder dangled a sword, which was held in its place by his leather waist-belt.

" 'Tis the General, mem," I whispered, standing still with consternation. " Whatever will we do?"

" Come on, and for pity's sake don't look as if you had seen a bogle. Leave the General to me. I would rather it were he than one of his long-faced officers. They say he likes to speak to a pretty woman, and for once I'll try to persuade myself that I can play the part."

AS SHE TALKED TO THE OLD MAN SHE WAS JUST INSPIRED

And, by my faith, she did !

What the minister and his elders of the Kirk of Kinneff would have thought could they have listened to my mistress's wiles as she talked to that old man, I do not know. She was just inspired. She spoke to him about many things—about the weather (it was by now raining old wives and pikestaffs), about his rheumatics, and about how he must miss his wife in this cold and inclement climate, and about the best remedies for rheumatic pains. And she begged leave to send him some rue and camomile from her garden to make a tisane for him to drink at bedtime. And she touched, ever so gently, on the straits they were in at the Castle, and hinted that it would not be long before he and his army could go home covered with glory with what they had done. And then she brought the conversation round, I know not how, to Edinburgh and her sister's wedding, and the sheets, and the fresh white lint which she had had to ask back from Mrs. Ogilvie, and how wet it was, and what a pity for the harvest.

And all the while I stood by shivering with terror, the weight of the Sceptre and the Sword of State pressing heavily on my shoulder.

By the time she had spoken it all, the General had handed her up on her horse, and had set us on our way with a salute and a bow, and a pleasant word of advice that we should change our wet things as soon as we got home.

" Oh, mistress, mistress !" I said, half laughing, half crying, when once we had passed the soldiers and were safe on our own quiet country road, " how could you do it, how could you think of the things to say ?"

" It was sheer desperation, Alison," she replied soberly. " The words just rose up in my mind, as if someone had put them there."

Late that night the rain cleared off and the mist lifted, and by one o'clock in the morning the moon was shining brightly in a clear sky. It shone in through the windows of the manse where Mrs. Grainger was watching the road that led to the kirkyard, in case anybody should pass that way and hear unusual sounds. It shone, also, through the windows of the kirk, and was a great help to the minister and me in the heavy job we were engaged in.

For though we had been successful in bringing the Honours of Scotland to the manse, it was not safe for them to bide there. So the minister had cast about in his mind for a secure hiding-place, and he had decided that no one was likely to look below the paving-stones in the kirk. So while Mrs. Grainger watched, her husband and me, with much ado, pulled out the oak boards that held up the pulpit, and lifted two of the great paving-stones which that erection covered. Then, hollowing out the earth and lime below them, we slipped in the precious treasures, carefully swathed in two of my mistress's best linen sheets. Covering them with a pailful of sawdust, and putting down the stones, and setting the pulpit to rights again, we left them to lie there for eight long years until the Restoration came, and King Charles the Second was brought back to his kingdom, and the Honours could be brought out in safety from under the floor and carried openly back to their proper resting-place in Edinburgh Castle.

XI

HOW THE QUEEN ESCAPED

IT was in the afternoon of a cold October day in the year 1567, that a mud-stained rider galloped into the little town of Kinross, which lies on the western shore of Lochleven, and, throwing his horse's bridle to a servant at the tiny inn, marched down to the water's edge.

"A boat, a boat!" he cried imperiously; "and make haste, thou lazy loons, for I carry a letter from my Lord Regent to the Queen's Majesty."

The boatmen looked at one another in perplexity, for the speaker was no other than George Douglas, youngest brother of Sir William of that name, who was Governor of Lochleven Castle, and as such was guardian or jailer, if we care to call him so, of the lovely and unfortunate Mary Queen of Scots, who was at the time imprisoned in the island stronghold.

It was no secret to anyone who lived in the neighbourhood that the young man, who had up till recently lived in the Castle, was devoted to the Queen, and was suspected, and with good reason, of planning her escape. Because of this, the Regent

Moray, who had shortly before visted his Royal half-sister, had ordered that he should be expelled from the Castle, and forbidden to return or to hold any communication with the unhappy captive.

Yet here he was, openly demanding a boat to take him across to the very place where by the authority of the Regent he was forbidden to go.

" But, Master George . . ." began one of the boatmen, who was instantly cut short by his impatient listener.

" I tell thee it is all right, Dickson," he cried. " See, here is my pass, signed by the Regent himself, and here is the letter bearing his own seal. But for Heaven's sake make haste—the matter brooks no delay."

Reassured by the sight of the seal on the letter, with the familiar arms of the Regent upon it, the man addressed as Dickson unshipped his oars, and the traveller was soon speeding across the narrow strip of water that separated the Castle from the mainland.

Not that Dickson was not glad to convey him thither, for George Douglas was a very great favourite with the country folk, whose sympathies were all with the imprisoned Queen; but it would have been as much as his head was worth to have rowed the young gentleman to the Castle without official permission.

13

Arrived at his destination, George was received by his widowed mother, who was at that time living in the fortress, with surprised delight. For he was her youngest son and her favourite. But after listening for a few minutes to her rehearsal of the small events which had taken place during his absence, he demanded to be taken to the presence of the Queen, giving as an excuse for his impatience the urgency of the business contained in the letter.

Accordingly Lady Douglas led him across the courtyard and up to the second story of the great tower or keep, where he found his. Royal mistress seated at her embroidery frame in a large, fairly comfortable room, which was separated from her bedroom by a wooden partition.

" George !" she cried, throwing down her needle, and advancing to meet him. " The Saints defend thee, but how hast thou come hither ? Methought thou hadst been banished by my brother's command."

" So I was, your Highness, and so will I be again," replied the young man, kneeling before his sovereign and kissing her hand, " for though my Lord Regent relaxed his ire sufficiently to entrust this letter, which is in answer to one of thine, to my hands, his heart has once more misgiven him, and if I am not mistaken there is a rider close

on my heels, who was bidden to reach the Castle
before me, and charge Sir William to have me
stopped on the shore and the letter taken from my
keeping there. So, as I have much to say to thee,
madam, and I will not be allowed to see thee, much
less to speak with thee again, let us leave the letter
for the present," and he flung it contemptuously
on the table, " and turn us to plan for thine escape,
while there is time."

Very hurriedly but very earnestly the two conspirators talked together, George Douglas trying
to encourage the captive by telling her of the
friends on shore who were scheming and plotting
for her escape, and impressing on her the part she
must play in the proceedings.

" I cannot be near your Highness," he went on,
" but there is another whom I deem as loyal
and trustworthy as myself. That is young Willie
Douglas, the orphan lad whom my brother, Sir
William, hath taken under his protection, and who
has charge of the boats. He is as deeply attached
to your Majesty as his knowledge of you will allow,
and if your Majesty have opportunity, and can
extend a little kindness to him, the lad will serve you
with all his power. And his power to serve you is
greater than that of most, for he is constantly coming
and going twixt the Castle and the shore. But,"
he added, looking through one of the deep-set

windows that overlooked the loch, " our brief interview will soon be at an end, for the messenger sent by the Earl of Moray to warn Sir William against me hath reached the shore, and is already on the loch. So if your Highness has any last commands for me, they must be short."

" And short they will be," said the Queen, rising to her feet, and going to a little aumbry cleverly contrived in one of the thick embrasures of the window. " I will straightway make a friend of little Willie Douglas. I know the lad's face, and have oftentimes been cheered by his smile, for he looks at me, when I am allowed to walk by the shore, with a world of sympathy in his eyes.

" And see, my trusty ally, though I have no commands, I have here two tokens to commit to thy care. One is this earring of mine; look, it is a bonny pearl, shaped like a pear, and not easily forgotten or copied. Carry it with thee, and when thy plans are matured and those of my other friends, find an occasion to send it back to me, and then I will know to be prepared.

" This other "—and she gave him a little folded handkerchief—" is a letter to my most loyal friend, Lord Seton. Yes, you may wonder," she went on as the young man unfolded the napkin, in the hope of finding some missive wrapped up in it ; " but now they allow me neither paper nor ink, so I must find some other means of script. So for ink I have the soot from the chimney, mixed with water—with practice one can write with it—while for paper I have naught to use but my finest cambric napkins which I brought with me from France."

A loud knocking at the outer gate of the Castle warned them that if the visitor were to escape arrest, or at least the possibility of being closely searched, he had better depart at once. So, bidding a hasty farewell to the Queen, he slipped down the spiral staircase which led to the ground floor of the tower, and, aided by his knowledge of the building, let himself out by a window and so gained the rocks where the rowing-boats lay.

The lad we have spoken of, a rosy-cheeked, dark-haired youth of about sixteen years of age, was there alone, and it needed but a word from his young master to persuade him to let him take one of the boats across to Kinross and leave it there, Willie promising to have it brought back in safety without any questions being asked. Thus he managed to leave the Castle in safety ere Lord Moray's messenger had grasped the fact that he had been there at all.

To plan an escape is one thing, to carry out the plan is another! All through that winter of 1567-68, as month succeeded month in uneventful monotony, and no pearl earring found its way back into her possession, the heart of Scotland's imprisoned Queen grew heavy as lead. She had done everything in her power to help on the plans of her friends on shore. She had taken pains, by kindly words, and occasionally little presents of money, to captivate Willie Douglas, who now worshipped the ground she trod on, and would have gladly risked his life to do her a service. She had tried to disarm any suspicions that might be felt about an attempt to escape, by calmly discussing the possibility with old Lady Douglas, who naturally thought that if the captive had any intention of risking such an adventure, she would have guarded her secret and held her tongue.

Indeed, the suggestion was treated so much as a joke, that both soldiers and servants, tired with the isolation and monotony of their lives, often joined in a game in which the pretended rescue of the Queen played the principal part. They would divide into two parties, one of which guarded the Castle, while the other tried to gain admittance.

One evening early in April Sir William had taken his prisoner, as he sometimes did, for a sail on the loch, and on their return they found the whole household thus engaged, while Lady Douglas, who was too old for such pranks, stood by looking on and laughing.

Even Queen Mary, in spite of her heavy heart,

could not help smiling as she watched the attacking party, who were in boats, pelting the would-be defenders with handfuls of mud and gravel.

" Methinks there would be danger of the prisoner escaping by the rear, forgotten by her captors," she said.

" Except that I should be there, your Majesty," replied Sir William rather grimly, as if he did not relish the turn the conversation had taken.

" I had forgotten that for the moment," rejoined the Queen lightly. " But what is that?" she exclaimed, shrinking back in her seat as the report of a gun rang out from one of the boats near the shore.

" It is that fool Drysdale, firing the old harquebus which lies in the boat in order to scare the wildfowl when they come too near the shore. Pray God it be but loaded with powder and not with shot, for he fired it point-blank among the crowd. See, he hath wounded two of my men, though both the knaves seem able to limp towards the Castle, What folly is this, Drysdale?" he asked severely. as, the boat having been rapidly rowed to the island, he jumped on shore and addressed the culprit, who happened to be no other than the captain of the garrison himself.

" 'Twas folly, I admit, Sir William," answered the man sheepishly, looking thoroughly ashamed of himself ; "but I had no thought than that the gun was loaded only with powder, and it seemed as if it would make the game more real if I fired it among the supposed enemy."

"And so thou hast wounded two of our best men," said his master sharply. "Let it serve as a lesson, and be done with this foolery. Let everyone go to their posts, and see to their duties," he cried, raising his voice, "and Drysdale, see thou to it that the wounded men be looked after and attended to by the Queen's chirurgeon."

The same evening that officer, who occupied a room directly above that of his Royal mistress, managed to get a word in private with her during the short half-hour when she was alone with her two maids of honour after she had supped and the rest of the household were having their evening meal in the hall below.

"Your Majesty," he began bluntly, "I now have it in my power to give you an opportunity which it behoves you to make use of. It happens that these two men whom Drysdale in his clumsiness hath so timeously wounded are the leaders of those who are always watching your every action and spying on your friends.

"Each of them hath a bullet in his leg, and, by'r Lady, it will not be my fault if their recovery is not slow and tedious, or if they leave their beds as long as it is to your advantage to have them left there."

"A thousand thanks for thy good offices, my friend," replied Mary sadly; "but if thou canst tell me how I can take advantage of them I shall be thy debtor. If I could get speech with George Douglas, we might maybe hatch some plot; but he is forbidden even to visit Kinross, and I have not had a word from him since before Yule. Little Willie Douglas sometimes managed to carry a letter when he went to and fro with the boats, but since that fox Drysdale saw me talking with him one morning in the courtyard, and afterwards found in the boy's pocket the louis d'or which I had given him for all the trouble and risk he ran (the old fox took it for himself—a malediction on him), the lad hath been watched so closely, besides being forbidden to cross to the shore, that I have been unable, except on one or two occasions, to send any message whatsoever to any of my friends."

"I heard a rumour two days ago that George Douglas, vexed by his banishment from Lochleven, was going to France," said the chirurgeon, "but I do not know if it is false or true."

"God grant it may be false," replied the Queen anxiously, tears coming into her eyes, "for if George Douglas leaves the country, then is my case hopeless indeed."

The rumour proved to be true, to all appearance at least, for some days later Lady Douglas entered the Queen's apartment in great agitation, holding an open letter in her hand.

" I have come to crave thine aid, your Majesty," she cried. "My luckless son hath sent me this letter to tell me that, tired of all the plotting and intrigue in this land, he hath determined to try his fortunes at the Court of France. As you know, he is my Benjamin, my best beloved, and I am an old woman now. I have written a reply, begging him to be content to remain in his own land—the Regent would surely find him work to do for my sake, if only the lad will have patience till the rival factions settle down."

The Queen smiled sadly at the old lady's words. Too well she knew that she was the bone of contention between the rival factions, and that as long as she remained in Scotland there was but little chance of their settling down.

" But what can I, a helpless prisoner do, to prevent thy son's going abroad?" she asked. "Had I been at liberty I would gladly have had him in my service, for he is a loyal and true friend, but, as thou knowest, my enemies have determined to keep him away from me."

" Perchance if your Majesty would write him a letter, begging him to remain in Scotland, he would listen to your words. I can send it with my own," said Lady Douglas, completely forgetting that in disobeying the strict injunction of the Regent that her youngest son should have no communication with the Queen, she was hardly acting fairly to her eldest son, Sir William, who was responsible for the safe keeping of that royal lady,

Write to George Douglas! At the thought of having the chance of so doing, the colour rose in Mary's cheeks, and she had much ado to keep her voice from trembling, for she had arranged a simple cipher with him, so that, while appearing to write an ordinary letter which anyone could read, she could in reality convey a far different message.

" I will gladly write to thy son, and beg him to stay at home, if thou thinkest he will pay any heed to my words," she answered, " though me-thinks thou makest too much of my influence. Thou canst read what I write, or show it to Sir William, so that he may have no fear of any plot between us."

Accordingly a letter was written by the Royal hand, and, after having been read by Lady Douglas and her son, was dispatched with that of the former to the impatient young man, now lingering in the neighbourhood of Kinross. But neither letter seemed to have any effect. He took no notice of that of the Queen, but wrote affectionately to his mother, stating that his mind was made up, and that, if she wanted to say farewell to him before his departure she must make an opportunity to meet him in the little town, and that immediately, as he intended to set out for France within four days.

So the poor old lady, who shed many tears on the receipt of this epistle, was rowed across to Kinross, and there took a sorrowful farewell of her son. As they parted he pulled a little packet wrapped loosely in dirty paper out of his pocket. Opening it, he displayed a pear-shaped earring.

" One of the boatmen found this on the shore of the island and brought it to me, offering to sell it for what I would give," he said, " but I knew it belonged to the Queen. She often wore a pair of these, and must have dropped this one when setting out for a sail with my father—at least, if the rascal found it where he said he did, otherwise he must have found an opportunity to steal it. Be that as it may, wilt thou return it to its owner, with my respects and the offer of my service."

" Much good thy service will do her with the sea betwixt thee," retorted Lady Douglas sharply, for she felt very angry and disappointed with this handsome son of hers. Nevertheless she took the earring and deposited it in one of her capacious pockets. When she arrived at the Castle she went straight to the Queen's apartment. Perhaps she felt more sure of sympathy there than in the chamber of her daughter-in-law, Sir William's wife, to whom a little daughter had been born just two days before.

" Now, well-a-day ! the headstrong lad hath gone," she sobbed, " and God alone knoweth when I shall see him again. Alack, your Majesty !" she added, " though I ken that it was the nobles' will that you should return to your native land, and you had little say in the matter, I find myself wishing many a time that you had bidden in France."

" And many a time I find myself wishing the same," replied Mary sadly, then, her kind heart; troubled at the sorrow she had been the unwilling cause of bringing to the old Countess, she knelt beside her and put her arms round her.

" Forgive me, madam," she said, " for being my father's daughter, for that was the beginning of the whole trouble." Her voice was so wistful that tears rose unbidden in the older woman's eyes, and she thrust her hand hurriedly into her pocket, seeking her handkerchief. Along with it she grasped the little packet her son had given her.

" Preserve me ! but I was forgetting," she cried,
pulling it out and drying her eyes. " Look what
a boatman found. Did you not mark its loss?
The rascal tried to sell it to my son, but he knew it
as yours, and demanded that it should be given
up. He entrusted it to me to be given to you
with the offer of his lasting service. Much good,
I told him, that would do you, while he was in
France and you in Lochleven Castle."

For a moment Mary could not trust herself to
answer, but light seemed to have come into the
gloomy chamber and joy into her heart. Here
was a token that George Douglas was *not* going
to France. On the contrary, he was lingering
near her, stirring up friends on her behalf, arranging
for her escape, and that shortly. For had it not
been arranged that the earring was to be returned
only to warn her to be ready ?

It was plain why he had announced his intention
of going abroad. Simply to allay suspicion, and
to obtain an interview with his mother, so that
he might enter into communication with her, the
Queen, and have an opportunity of sending her
this token.

To gain time to collect her thoughts, she stood
for a moment turning the ornament over and over
in her hand. " It was good of him to be so mindful," she said at last, her voice quite steady now,

" for I would have grieved had I lost this. It belonged to my grandmother of Guise."

" When doth your son set out for France?" she added, speaking quite casually, almost as if she had forgotten the subject of which his mother's heart was so full.

" When he actually takes boat I know not, but he mentioned that he was riding to Glasgow to-morrow night, and that it was not his intention to return to Kinross."

" Riding to Glasgow tomorrow night!" Once more the quick colour flashed into Mary's face, and she was fain to turn it away from Lady Douglas's keen eyes. For those were the words that had been agreed on to let her know the day and hour when she must hold herself ready for the great adventure.

She was glad when her kindly old visitor bade her good-night, and her two waiting-maidens came into the room, evidently greatly excited over some unwonted happening. They were devoted to their mistress, and shared in all her hopes and fears.

" Something unusual must be afoot, your Majesty," said Janet Kennedy, the elder of the two, " for young Willie Douglas hath bidden the whole household, from the Governor and old Lady Douglas down to little Margaret, who is but six

years old, to a *déjeuner* tomorrow at midday, after
which the maddest revels have to take place,
Willie himself acting the part of the Abbot of
Misrule. For some reason, the feast is not to be
held in the great hall, but in the smaller guest-
chamber on the other side of the courtyard. Sir
William hath given his consent to Willie's request;
perchance he thinks it may divert his mother's
attention from the departure of her youngest son."

" But, your Majesty "—and here the young girl
lowered her voice, and looked anxiously round the
apartment as if afraid that the very walls might
echo her words—" if Willie Douglas hath no other
meaning than a simple revel he is an impudent
varlet, for he bade me seek your Highness's ear, and
whisper into it that he hath need of siller to carry
out his plan."

" And siller he shall have," said the Queen,
rising in evident excitement, and opening a casket
in which, concealed in a secret drawer, was a
considerable sum of money. " Here, Janet, give
this to him secretly — secretly, I say — for thou
knowest not—indeed I know not myself—how much
hangs upon his plan. And now, my maids, let
us compose ourselves, and talk of other matters,
for it will soon be time to sup, and supper often
brings, as thou knowest, an evening visit from our
jailer, Sir William."

Sure enough, Sir William appeared with the evening meal, which the Queen, as a special favour was allowed to partake of in her own room along with her maids—the rest of the household supping together in the great hall immediately afterwards.

He told his prisoner, in his ponderous way, of the morrow's festivities, to which, indeed, he seemed to be quite looking forward, and explained that Willie had begged that the *déjeuner* should be set in the smaller guest-chamber, as he wished to prepare various little surprises for his guests, which explanation appeared to satisfy the simple mind of Sir William, who was a very unsuspicious man, but the Queen's quicker wits saw at once another reason.

For while the window of the great hall looked straight across to Kinross, and any unusual happenings there would be seen by those within, the windows of the guest-chamber looked away in the other direction, and from them nothing was visible but a wide expanse of wood and water.

By noon next day the whole of the inhabitants of the Castle were in wild excitement. Willie had certainly played his part well, and provided, not only an excellent meal, but many newfangled surprises and frolics.

There was a fortune-teller, whom no one could

recognize, who claimed that he could unfold the future; and there was a necromancer, who looked like the Evil One himself, who put one of the wee spotted chickens which were the delight of old Tibbie the henwife's heart, into his own pocket, and, after many turnings and twistings of his body and wavings of his hands, lifted it out of the folds of the lace kerchief which young Lady Douglas wore round her shoulders.

Finally, there was a search all over the Castle for "hidden treasure," which turned out to be two merks hidden in a snuff-mull under the root of an old thorn tree in the garden. It was while they were searching for this that the Master of the Revels managed to cross the Queen's path when she was out of earshot of anyone else, and whisper to her in passing that she should be ready to slip down the stairs and leave the Castle with one of her waiting-maids, while the household were at supper. "I've borrowed some country woman's clothes," he muttered; "Janet Kennedy will find them lying in an old cask in the cellar; put them on, and let Janet watch from the window for my signal. If I have managed to get the key I will hold up my right hand. If I hold up my left then your Highness must make shift to get out of the window. I will set two oars up against it, which may serve in lieu of a ladder."

Mary took part in the revels as long as possible, then, feeling her need of rest, for she had not closed an eye the night before, she withdrew to her chamber, accompanied by young Lady Douglas, for she was seldom left alone. She threw herself on her bed, and the Mistress of the Castle, seeing that she was not inclined for conversation, called in the old woman who kept the inn at Kinross, who had brought some milk and eggs to the Castle to help in the preparations for the feast, and sat down to indulge in a good gossip.

Mary took little notice of the talk at first, but her attention was aroused by hearing George Douglas named.

"Aye, he is still in the neighbourhood, your Ladyship. I saw him yesterday wi' my ain een col-louging* with my Lord Seton and my Lord Beaton, who, it seems, were passing through Kinross on their way to the Assize Court at Glasgow," said the old innkeeper. "Folk have said that my Lord Beaton and my Lord Seton were at daggers drawn, but they must have found some way of composing their differences."

Well did Mary know what it was that had induced these haughty noblemen to sink their differences and join together in a mutual endeavour. It was loyalty to her person, it was in order to effect her escape !

* Collouge, to whisper together.

The knowledge that they were actually in the neighbourhood, waiting and watching for the boat that would bring her ashore, was almost too much for her. She felt that she would suffocate within the four walls of a room, she must go outside and see what was to be seen on shore.

" I would fain take the air," she said, " for my head feels dull and heavy, and I have a sore throbbing in my temples."

" In good sooth, your Majesty looks flushed and feverish," replied young Lady Douglas, looking at her anxiously. " I trust you have not been chilled carrying out all that mad boy's capers."

" No, it is not a chill, it is merely that this chamber is hot now that the sun beats on the windows. My cheeks will cool once I am in the fresh air."

Old Lady Douglas joined the Queen in the garden, for she was not allowed to go beyond the courtyard unattended, and together they paced up and down the terrace which looked across to the little town of Kinross.

" Do my eyes deceive me ? Or is yon a body of horsemen ?" cried the old lady suddenly. " Hey ! there is no doubt of it, I saw the sun glinting on their armour as they came out of the wood. See, they are riding towards Kinross—there must be twenty of them. I must raise an alarm, someone must go ashore at once, for dear only knows what their purpose may be."

The Queen looked in the direction in which the excited old woman was pointing, and was just in time to see the last of a body of soldiers disappearing behind a low hill.   Quick as thought she set herself to change the conversation and to divert the old lady's mind.

" If there is an Assize at Glasgow, doubtless many riders are abroad," she replied carelessly, and then she began to enquire about tales of long ago, when Lady Douglas was young, and she herself a child at Inchmahome, and the older woman was soon quite absorbed in bygone memories, quite forgetful of what might be passing on shore.   For over an hour they paced up and down, and the old lady was quite astonished, though the clever Queen was not, when Sir William came towards them with the news that her Majesty's supper was served, and that he had been waiting some time to escort her to her room.

Here another danger awaited her, for Sir William, happening to glance out of the window, discovered Willie Douglas just below him busily engaged in examining, or so it seemed to him, the chains by which the boats were moored to the little pier.

" What art thou doing there, thou fool ?   The boats are fast enough and do not need thy meddling.

Be off at once, it is almost dark, and no time for a smatchet like thee to be fiddling with the chains."

A chill of fear gripped Mary's heart. She knew what Willie Douglas was about, for they had spoken of such an enterprise, when they had little hope of ever being able to carry it out. He was putting wooden pegs into the fastening of the chains of all the boats but one, so that, when the Queen's escape was discovered and pursuit organized, it would be very difficult to unfasten them.

Once more her quick wit came to her aid. "Oh, Sir William!" she exclaimed, sinking back on the settle in the corner farthest from the window, "methinks these revels have been too much for me, for first my head was hot and heavy, and I was fain to take the air, and now I am as cold as lead, and like to fall into a swoon. Send one of my maidens, an it please thee, for a tasse * of wine."

Sir William gazed wildly about for one of the two waiting-maids, for he was none too fond of attending to swooning women, even though this one happened to be a Queen, but neither maid was there. Of course the Queen knew that. So he was fain to go himself—and by the time he had returned and the Queen had drunk the wine, the

* Cup.

question of what Willie Douglas had been doing had gone clean out of his head.

He served the Queen ceremoniously while she supped, then went to join the rest of the household at their evening meal in the great hall below, leaving his little daughter and her cousin with the Royal party, a very usual arrangement, for it was felt that the quick eyes of these children would notice any unusual happenings in the room.

But the Queen had already planned how to escape from their curious eyes. As we have seen, the room directly above hers was occupied by her chirurgeon, and she had directed Janet Kennedy to take the clothes provided by Willie Douglas up to this apartment, and to confide to him the news that an escape was to be attempted that evening. As he supped with the household, his chamber would be empty just when the Queen required it, and, by keeping his eyes open and his wits alert, he could perhaps help Willie Douglas in whatever plans he had laid to obtain possession of the keys of the Castle.

Accordingly, when the clatter of dishes let her know that the party below had commenced supper, she announced that she wished to say her evening prayers as she intended to go early to bed, and, as the chirurgeon was absent from his room and it was quieter there, she would go upstairs for a little

time with Janet Kennedy, while Maria Courcelles
would stay with the little girls, and have a game
of tod-in-the-hole. The children, delighted at
this arrangement, for they loved the game, and
quite accustomed to the Queen's habit of observing
stated times of prayer, settled down on each side
of the good-natured Maria, while Queen Mary
and Janet sped noiselessly upstairs, and arrayed
themselves hastily in the dark-coloured kirtles and
hoods which turned them into a couple of douse-
looking country women.

Meanwhile down in the hall supper was pro-
ceeding as usual. At the head of a small table
set on a dais sat Sir William Douglas, the keys of
the Castle, five of them, hung on a chain, lying on
the table beside him, for as the members of the
guard supped with the rest of the household at
this hour, it was the custom that the outer doors
and gates should be locked and the keys brought
into the hall. Beside him sat his wife and other
relatives, also the Queen's medical attendant.
The other inhabitants of the Castle, soldiers,
servants, and boatmen, supped at the great table
below the dais, in the centre of the hall.

The first course was eaten among genial jokes
and laughter, for the day's revels had put everyone
in good humour. Then came the second course,
and Willie Douglas, waiting at the Governor's

table, brought in a massive dish of stewed capons. As a well-trained page, he carried a napkin over his left arm, and as he set down the capons before his master the napkin slipped from his arm and dropped, as if by accident, on the keys, a corner of it falling into the gravy in the dish. The chirurgeon, whose keen eyes noticed the incident, instantly began to talk with great earnestness about some points of medicine, in which he knew Sir William was interested, and that good .man, who, as we have seen, was peculiarly unsuspicious, joined in the conversation with such intense interest that he forgot, for the moment, the tasty dish steaming under his nose. Meanwhile the page, with great deliberation, though, if anyone had noticed it, with a very shaky hand, drew the corner of the napkin out of the dish, and, crumpling it together, retired quickly from the hall, as if to go in search of a clean one. Meanwhile the conversation between the chirurgeon and the Governor grew more and more animated ; everyone was listening, so the incident passed unheeded.

Upstairs in the chirurgeon's room two women, clad in country hoods and kirtles, over which were thrown long dark cloaks, stood counting the minutes with trembling breath. Janet Kennedy was by the tiny window, the Queen beside the half-open door. Up the staircase came the sound of the merry voice of Maria Courcelles, playing with the children, further away still sounded faintly the voices in the great hall.

" He is out—he has given the signal," whispered Janet. " Let us go at once, and may the Saints aid and defend us !"

Swiftly and noiselessly the two shadowy figures slipped down the winding newel staircase, past the room where Maria and the two little Douglases were, past the hall with its loud voices and rattle of dishes, through the deserted entrance hall, littered with pieces of armour and weapons of sport, and out of the great door, beside which Willie was standing, and which he locked behind them with a sigh of relief.

" I oiled it last night," he muttered, as they stole down the rocky shore to where the boats were moored. " I rose at midnight when the guards were all asleep."

In another moment they were in a boat and had cast off from the island, Willie pulling one oar, Janet another, while the Queen lay in the stern so as to be hidden from observation. When they had rowed about a furlong out, Willie drew the keys from his pocket, and flung them into the loch. " 'Twill be long enough before they lay hands on these again," he laughed, " and, as all the doors are locked, it will take Sir William and his men some little time to find a way out of the Castle. Doubtless they will jump out of the windows, but most of them are barred, and even when they do, I have taken good care that they will find the boats ill to launch. I drove a gimlet twice through the bottom of each of them, as well as fouling the chains.

" Stand up, your Majesty," he said presently, " and wave to the shore. For there are watchers there waiting to make sure you are in the boat ere they give the signal to the horsemen who are gathered in readiness up there on the hillside."

With a glad little cry, Mary sprang to her feet, and, standing in the prow of the boat, drew forth her white veil bordered with crimson and gold, which had been hidden by the dark hood, and waved it above her head, tears of joy running down her cheeks meanwhile. Instantly a man, who seemed to have been lying on his face on the shore, sprang to his feet, and gave a signal to someone in the rear. Then a rider was seen to spring to his saddle and gallop away in the evening mist.

The main body of men could not have been far distant, for, as the boat approached the land, little groups of horsemen came galloping down from all directions, their heads uncovered, their daggers drawn.

George Douglas was there, eager to be the first

to greet his Queen. Lord Beaton was there, and Lord Seton, and Lord Herries, and the gallant Master of Sempill, husband of Mary Livingstone, who had been one of the Queen's Maries.

" But how could so many men gather ?" asked Mary in amazement. " I expected one or two, but methinks this is a little army, wellnigh a hundred strong."

" The good folk of Kinross are loyal to your Highness," replied Willie proudly, " and many a guidman and guidwife have risked the vengeance of your enemies by harbouring your friends 'neath their roofs these two nights past. Aye, and they have sheltered the horses in outbye stables for ten or twenty miles round, and given them what old oats they had, so that they may be fit and ready for hard riding."

As he spoke, the boat grated on the gravel of the shore, and willing hands drew her in. Disdaining their help, the Queen jumped ashore, and, half crying, half laughing with excitement and joy, held out her hand for her triumphant followers to kiss. But there was little time for ceremony. At any moment pursuit from the Castle might begin, and, although the Queen was once more free, she was surrounded by danger on every hand.

A number of horses, the fleetest that could be found in the length and breadth of Scotland, stood

THE QUEEN JUMPED ASHORE

ready, and Mary and her companions were soon
mounted, and, with the loyal nobles at their sides
and surrounded by their followers, rode briskly
through the little town, the simple townsfolk, delighted at the success of their enterprise, crowding
to their doorways and crying blessings on the
Queen as she passed.   Once in the open country,
they set spurs to their horses, and, ere night had
completely fallen, the fair young Queen of Scots,
for even now she was only twenty-five, was safely
lodged in the Castle of West Niddrie in Fife, the
seat of the Earl of Seton.

XII

THE LASSIE WITH THE LANTERN

THE red glow of a stormy sunset was shining into a large, comfortable room in the Castle of Redbraes in Berwickshire in the autumn of the year 1682. Its occupants were Sir Patrick Hume, the owner of the Castle, his wife, and his eldest daughter, Grizel.

Lady Hume was sitting in a great chair by the fire, knitting placidly, and every now and then joining, by a word, in the animated conversation which was being carried on by her husband and daughter. They were discussing politics, for these were troublous times in the history of our land, when there was reason to fear that the old and hated faith of the Roman Church might be brought back to be the established religion of the country.

Sir Patrick, as well as many of his friends, was a staunch Presbyterian, and had lately brought suspicion upon himself by meeting with several prominent English noblemen who were known to be leaders of the Protestant party, and discussing with them what could best be done to ward off the threatened danger. Indeed, so conspicuous had he made himself that, when a plot was discovered in London against the life of the King, Charles II., and his brother the Duke of York, those in high places suspected that Sir Patrick had been privy to it, which was utterly untrue, and a rumour had even reached Redbraes that a price had been put upon its master's head.

But up till now Sir Patrick had laughed at the rumour, declaring that he was much too unimportant a person for anyone to want to arrest. He had just been repeating this opinion to his wife and daughter who took a more serious view of the situation than he did, when the door opened, and a good-looking boy of about twelve entered the room carrying a small sealed paper, which he held out to his father.

" Hullo, Rob, and what may this be ? A letter from George Baillie of Jarviswood, perhaps, about the fillies that he and I bought at Michaelmas tryst."

" Nay, Father, not from Jarviswood," answered Rob ; " a laddie brought it over the hill, and I think he came from Hallyburton ; but there is no address on the letter, so I cannot tell whether it comes from Cousin John Hume or not."

" We shall soon see," said Sir Patrick, breaking the seal and unfolding the letter.

As he did so, his face changed. For there was

no writing whatever on the paper, all that it contained was a woodcock's feather. He turned it over and over in silence for a moment, then he said gravely, " Whoever sent this meant it for a warning. It is a token that I must fly. So it would seem, my sweethearts, that you have read the signs of the times better than I. Go and tell the laddie, Rob, to return from whence he came, and to say to them that sent him that I have received the letter and will attend to its contents."

" He didna wait," said Rob, " he just handed me the letter—I was down by the burnside—then he ran away."

"Better so, better so," repeated Sir Patrick; " the fewer that have to do with this affair the better. So perchance 'twere best for thee to run away also, Rob. Thy mother and I have much to talk about, and Grizel here can help us. But listen to me, my son. Thou art a big lad now, with plenty of sense. Say nothing to anyone about this letter, and keep a quiet-tongue in thy head if I chance to be away from Redbraes by the morning. I can trust thee, Rob ?"

" Aye, Father, thou canst trust me," said Rob steadily, and taking one long look at his father, but asking no further question, he turned and left the room.

" I must be off at once," said Sir Patrick the

moment the door was shut, "for Jimmie Winter told me this morning that he had heard that a party of dragoons rode into Duns last night and were quartered there. But, fool that I was, I paid no heed to the tale."

"But where canst thou go?" asked Lady Hume anxiously, her face growing pale at the danger which, it was only too evident, threatened her husband. "If thou take to the hills they may find thee, and doubtless by this time all the high-roads will be watched. Else couldst thou have endeavoured to reach Berwick or Leith, and thus have escaped overseas till the storm blows by."

Sir Patrick shook his head. "If so be that the dragoons are after me," he sighed, "all such roads to escape will be blocked. Is there no hidey-hole nearer home that we can think of? Could I have gotten to the coast I might have hidden in one of the caves that can only be reached at ebb tide, but it fears me that is out of the question now that the hounds have been set on my track."

"I have it, Father," cried Grizel, springing up from the low stool on which she had been seated: "why not hide in the vault under the kirk? I doubt if even the King's dragoons will be fearless enough to risk meeting a ghost by looking for thee in such an awesome place. 'Tis true thou wouldst be wellnigh frozen with cold, especially at this time of year, but there is room for thee to stretch thy legs, for it runs under the whole length of the kirk, and we could bring thee thy food, and warm things to lie in."

" By my soul ! Grizel, but thou art a lass to be proud of," said Sir Patrick, his eyes shining, while Lady Polwarth came and put her arm round her daughter, as if to gain strength and courage from the mere bodily touch.

" Do not delay for one moment, Patrick," she went on anxiously ; "thou canst step out by the side door and go through the wood to the kirk-yaird.   Once inside the vault thou art safe.   Thou art the only person who has the key.   Lock the iron door on the inside, and if we need it thou canst hand it out by the little slit in the wall, low down in the gable end of the kirk.   Folk think that is there to ventilate the kirk ; it is lucky that few of them realize that its purpose is to let air into our vault."

" Yes, Father, get away at once.   If the Dragoons are out, they may be here at any moment.   I wish that thou hadst had thy supper, but we cannot help that.   I'll slip down with it after the bairns have gone to bed and there is no one about.   And we'll tell Jimmie Winter the whole story, he is to be trusted like one of ourselves.   He will help Mother and me to carry down some bedding and a mattress for thee to lie on. We'll come quite late at night when everyone else, even the men about the place, have gone to bed."

So the matter was settled, and in half an hour's time the Master of Redbraes Castle, having left the house unobserved, was safely lodged in his family vault. Some three hours later a slender figure, wearing a long black cloak, the hood of which was drawn closely over her head, might have been seen, by a close observer, to leave the Castle by the little side door and vanish into the plantation of thickly planted fir trees that stretched almost all the way between the Castle and the church. It was Grizel Hume, and under her cloak she carried in one hand a basket containing food enough to serve her father for twenty-four hours, and a bottle of wine to quench his thirst; in the other, a little roughly fashioned three-sided lantern, which was lit, but which she only intended to bring from under her cloak if necessity arose, for she had no wish to raise a rumour that a will-o'-the-wisp had been seen among the tombstones. Slowly picking her steps among the protruding roots of the fir trees, she had wellnigh reached the gate leading into the churchyard when a most unwelcome noise broke on her ear.

She was now near the manse, and the minister's old dog, Trusty, had heard the rustle of her foot-

steps among the fallen leaves and was now giving
voice to his curiosity. "What a mercy he is shut
up!" said Grizel to herself; "but a way must be
found to stop him. No one is likely to heed him
tonight, and I will creep by and hide behind
a tombstone till he grows weary of his own noise;
but if he barks every night when I come past, the
minister will notice, and will watch to see what is
the matter."

It was as she thought. In a few minutes the
dog quieted down, and she was at liberty to step
through among the tombstones, her breath coming
in little anxious gasps as she did so, for, to a young
girl of her age, it was a weird and ghostly walk.
But the dead slept quietly under the grass, and
nothing stirred save a great tawny owl which was
perched on one of the branches of a wide-spreading
tree, and which flew off with such an uncanny
screech, that Grizel nearly dropped both basket
and lantern.

Her father was waiting to open the heavy iron
door for her, for he had heard the dog at the
manse barking and had guessed the cause.

"Didst think the screech owl was a ghost, my
lassie?" he asked tenderly, as he groped in the
darkness of the vault to take the heavy cloak from
her shoulders.

"It made me jump," acknowledged Grizel,

IT WAS A WEIRD AND GHOSTLY WALK

with a little laugh, " but I wasna what you might call feared. But wait a minute, Father ; we must put something over the lantern till we can hang up this bit of black stuff which I have brought with· me over that slit of a window. It would never do for any passer-by to see even a glimmer of light coming out of the Laird's vault. That would put the whole countryside a-clavering about body-snatching and suchlike nonsense."

" Thou art right, sweetheart, as thou art ever," replied Sir Patrick, and he sheltered the tiny lantern under his coat until the girl had satisfied herself that every chink and crevice of the tiny apartment was completely hidden by the cloth.

" 'Twill keep the light in, but 'twill keep the air out," she said anxiously. " But as thou canst not have it there in the daytime, in case folk might notice something queer about the opening, we can have it at night, for I mean to come always and sit with thee for an hour or two ; 'twill wile away the time, and thou canst sleep during the day."

Sir Patrick looked round his dreary abode with rather a doleful smile. The stone-flagged floor was damp and shiny ; the stone coffins, each lying on its ledge were but sad company; a human skull, centuries old, maybe, which had been dug up in the churchyard and now occupied a niche near the window, added to the awesomeness of the place. It might be a secure refuge, but it was a depressing one for a hunted man to hide in. Grizel, with her ready tact, understood this.

" Here is thy supper, Father," she said cheerfully, beginning to unpack her basket : " roasted potatoes —I did them in the embers after our own supper, and told little Sandy, who, as thou knowest, is always asking questions, that I wanted them to give to a poor man whom I had seen out in the cold. Thou wert the poor man, and I saw thee with the eyes of my imagination. So it wasna just a lie—and cold mutton—it was cold anyway, and I dare not get the serving-maids to make anything hot. They would have been asking questions next. But after this we'll always have a warm supper—and a lump of currant dumpling —you like that—and. a bottle of the best claret ; I brought thee the best, just for a treat. And while thou art eating thy supper, I'll measure the clear spaces of the floor between those coffins. Aye, I thought so," she went on, walking up and down, measuring the floor by her steps. "There will just be room in this corner for the old black walnut bedstead that lies up in the back garret. Maybe thou hast forgotten it, but Mother thought of it at once. The legs of it fold up, and the ends fold down, so that Jimmie Winter and I can easily

THE LASSIE WITH THE LANTERN 223

carry it between us. With a good mattress and plenty of blankets thou canst be almost as snug and warm as in thine own bed at home."

In the small hours of the next morning, if anyone had been abroad, they would have imagined that someone was flitting from Redbraes, for they would have met a strange little procession, consisting of three persons. First came Grizel and the household factotum, Jimmie Winter, carrying between them an ancient black bedstead; while Lady Hume, laden with a bundle of blankets, well hidden under a dark coverlet, brought up the rear. The perilous journey was repeated, and this time a mattress and a good stock of food were added, and when, just before the moon rose in the early morning, the two ladies and the old servant retraced their steps to the Castle, they had the satisfaction to know that they had made Sir Patrick as comfortable as he could be in the circumstances.

Daylight brought good evidence that he had not escaped a moment too soon, for the household at Redbraes had hardly finished breakfast when a party of Dragoons rode up, and searched the Castle from garret to dungeon, opening every press and cupboard, and even running their swords through the feather-beds, in case the master of the house should be concealed beneath them. One of them, who had been set to guard the front door, let fall a word to Jimmie Winter that Sir Patrick's friend and neighbour, George Baillie of Jerviswood, had been arrested in his own house the evening before, and was now on his way to the Tolbooth in Edinburgh, under the escort of ten of their companions.

When the soldiers rode away to search the surrounding country, Lady Hume and her daughter watched them anxiously. Would they look into the church, or would they pass it by? They halted at the manse, and paid the minister and his wife a visit, apparently searching that house also, for they spent a considerable time there; then they disappeared down the road that led to the church.

"There's a soldier has ridden up to the kirk and is looking in at the window," cried Sandy, who, too young to understand the danger, was watching the doings of the dragoons with great delight from the green in front of the Castle.

Lady Hume caught her breath with a little sob, but Grizel made no sign. "He hasna thought it worth his while to go into the kirk," she said calmly and clearly, so that any curious servant could hear her words. "He's away after the others. Doubtless Mr. Holiwell told him that there is not cover for a mouse, let alone a man, in our kirk."

THE LASSIE WITH THE LANTERN 225

But, in spite of the girl's brave words, her mother could see that she was troubled, and made an excuse to retire to her own little sitting-room, asking Grizel to follow with an armful of household linen. "What is it, my lass?" she asked, when Grizel had laid the linen on the table and shut the door. "What are you feared for now? To my mind the danger is past, once they are satisfied that he is not in the Castle."

"It's not the dragoons, Mother, it's Mr. Holiwell's dog. I must take food to Father every night, and sit with him for an hour or two, just to pass the time, for it's too dark for him either to write or to read in there. And though we lit the lantern last night, I would not do it often. If that dog barks every night as I go by, folk will wonder, and maybe come out to see who is about at so late an hour. A plague on the beast. It's old and doddered; I wish we could poison it."

"We cannot do that," replied Lady Hume, "but I have been thinking over the matter. If thou wilt see to thy father, I think I can manage the dog. As thou knowest, the mistress of the manse has a horror of mad dogs. She once saw one when she was young, and the dread of seeing another comes between her and her wits. I'll drop a word to Jimmie Winter to spread that rumour that we heard last month

that one has been seen on the hill, over the Duns
way, and I myself will carry the rumour to the
manse, and I'll be much astonished if old Trusty
does not get a wee thing poison in his porridge,
just to make certain he doesna go mad also.
His mistress told me the other day she had
noticed a fleck of froth at his mouth, and there
being no reason at that time that I should say
anything else, I suggested that maybe the beast
had not had dog's ill when he was young ; but now
I'll mention with great concern the mad dog
that Jimmie has heard tell of."

Grizel laughed. "Poor old Trusty," she
said. " I'm afraid his doom is sealed. For your
tongue would wile a bird from the lift, Mother.
But he is so crabbit and cross, he is not safe
nowadays, and it would be a kindness to the
poor beast himself to put him out of the way."

And sure enough, tho' the minister's wife
made no remark after Lady Hume had told
the tale, Trusty's kennel was empty in the
morning, and he was never heard to bark again.

Every night after that, in fair weather or foul,
when everyone else had gone to bed, Grizel
slipped out of the Castle, carrying her little
lantern and a stock of provisions under her
cloak, and threaded her way among the dark
fir trees and through the tombstones in the

churchyard, and spent the midnight hours with her father in his cold and lonely abode, coming back in the early morning before the dawn broke or anyone else was astir. In after years she often declared that the homeward journey was more weird and uncanny than the walk to the kirk the night before.

After that first evening the lantern was seldom lit, in case any stray beam was seen from outside, and father and daughter would sit close together in the darkness, or in the faint light afforded by moon or stars, and cheer each other up by telling all the funny little happenings that had occurred in Castle or vault during the day.

One night Grizel found her father in a particularly cheerful mood. "Though thou mayst not believe it, Grizel," he said, "I have found a companion here, and I trow he will prove a great blessing to me, though he gave me a bit of a fright at first."

"Oh, Father! dinna say it's a ratten," cried Grizel, springing to her feet, and speaking louder than was wise under the circumstances. "Thou knowest how I hate them, an' if there are rattens here, I will aye be feared they may be nibbling at thy toes while thou art sleeping."

"Houts! lassie. They would be as likely to nibble at my nose without wakening me. Put a notion like that out of thy sensible head. No, no; it's not a ratten, it's just a nice sleek little mouse, and of all places in the world canst thou guess where it has chosen to make its nest? Under that skull in the niche! This forenoon, as I was lying snug in bed, with my eyes fixed on it, wondering what kind of soul had used it for a dwelling—for solemn thoughts come to one when they live in a place like this, my girl— if I didna see it move, and for a moment, I'm not ashamed to say, my heart leapt into my mouth. Then what should peep out but the bright eyes and pointed nose of the bonniest wee mouse that ever I saw. It vanished at once at the sight of me, but, with the help of some crumbs of bread and a morsel of cheese, I warrant we will be the best of friends in a week's time."

The next Sunday night Sir Patrick was chuckling to himself again. "Dull, Grizel?" he said, in answer to her anxious enquiry as to how he got through the long, lonely hours. "How can I be dull, when every Sunday I hear not only two long sermons, but psalms and prayers as well? The boards in the ceiling are loose at yon end of the vault, so I push one aside a wee chink, and sit on that raised stone. I find myself stationed just below the pulpit, and when good Mr. Holiwell prays for all prisoners and captives, and all who are in danger or distress, I know he hath me in his mind, and it cheers me greatly. And then when the preaching is over and the folk go out, they stand about in the kirkyaird, as thou knowest, and tell each other all the news there is to tell. So when I hear them making a move up above, I tiptoe softly over and crouch down below that slit of a window, and by the time the last of them has left the kirkyaird, I know the whole clavers of the countryside. No longer ago than this forenoon I heard Sandy Douglas, standing within two yards of my head, speiring of Jimmie Winter if he had ' any idea where Sir Patrick is ?' and ' if he had got clear away out of the country ?'

"Jimmie, honest man, had much ado to stick to the truth and yet put him off the scent. He said, and very truly, that if the dragoons had got hold of the Laird, everybody would have heard of it ere now, and that, if her Ladyship kens where her husband is, she hasna made anybody else the wiser. By my faith, Grizel, I could have found it in my heart to have shouted out, ' I'm here, Sandy !' just to have made the old man jump."

A few days afterwards it was Grizel's turn to cause the merriment. " We must have the lantern lit tonight, Father," she said, when the iron door was closed, and she was beginning to set out the contents of the basket. " For see what I have brought thee ! A whole sheep's head, with hardly a bite of meat taken off it. Mother ordered it, for she knew how much you like it, and she thought the broth would do for the bairns. I dare not take it off the plate as long as Tibbie was in the room, for very little would make the serving-maids suspect, but when she was gone, and the bairns were busy with their broth, I lifted the cover, and slipped the whole head on to a plate I had in my lap, underneath my apron. There was a gigot of mutton at my mother's end of the table, but thou knowest how much little Sandy likes sheep's head. Thou shouldst have seen his face when he had finished his broth and his eyes fell on the empty dish.

" ' Oh, Mother !' he cried, as piteous like as if he had not tasted food all day, ' will ye look at Grizel? While we have been supping our broth, she has eaten the whole sheep's head, bones and all.' And he would not be content with the mutton, but girned on about the sheep's head till Rob gave him a handful of sweeties, and then he forgot all about it.

" I think Rob and Christian suspect something," she added, " for they must have known I couldna have eaten a whole sheep's head. But they made no remark, and, as I say, Rob sacrificed his whole week's stock of sweeties to keep Sandy's tongue quiet."

"Rob is a good lad," replied Sir Patrick, "and sensible for his years. I trust I may live to tell him so someday."

"And I trust that I may live to explain to Sandy that I am not so greedy as he thought I was," laughed Grizel, watching her father making a hearty supper from the dish she had so cleverly secured.

As the weeks went past, and a rumour, which was not believed at first, that the dragoons had left the neighbourhood, proved true, Sir Patrick grew restless, and at last announced his intention of returning to his own house. "I can sit about in thy mother's parlour," he protested, "and slip into the closet off it, when any of the servants are about."

But his wise daughter shook her head. "We must have a more secure hiding-place than that, Father. Have patience for a few days more, till Mother and I can have a talk with Jimmie Winter."

It was Lady Hume who thought of the next step. "I have it," she said, as Grizel and Jimmie and she sat over the fire in the gloaming next evening, Jimmie having been brought into her room under the excuse of mending a broken spring in her easy chair. " Thou knowest that bedroom that we never use on the ground floor in the west wing, the room that has the little bed in the corner. The bed is easily moved, so what is to hinder us loosening the flooring below it and digging a hole deep enough to hold your father. Jimmie can make a box to fit it, or we can bring the big blanket kist down from the garret. It is both deep and wide, and we can fit it up with a feather-bed and blankets, and put a few holes in the lid, and when once your father pops in there, and we put the flooring down, and the bed back in its place, who will ever think of looking under it ?"

So Sir Patrick had to endure some lonely nights, when Grizel only took time to carry a basket of food to him, then hurried back to Redbraes to spend the small hours of the morning helping Jimmie Winter to dig a hole in the ground under the floor of the bedroom in the west wing. One could hardly call it digging, scraping would answer the description better, for as they dare not use a spade or any other tool, in case the servants might hear them, they scraped up the earth with their fingers, putting it into a sheet spread on the floor beside them, and carried it out of the window, scattering it over the garden beds.

By the time the hole was large enough to hold the blanket kist, Grizel's nails were worn down to the quick, but she took little heed of the pain when she had her father once more at Redbraes, tho' he had to be careful not to let anyone know that he was in the house. But it was easier to take care of him at home, even though he spent most of his time in the little closet that entered from his wife's room, and of which she alone had the key.

The hole in the floor was only meant for a refuge in case dragoons arrived suddenly, or in any other emergency. But Grizel, who was afraid that in wet weather water might come through the earth and trickle into the hole, went every morning to look at it. Alas! scarcely more than a week had passed after Sir Patrick's return before her fears were realized. One night it rained in torrents, and when she went as usual the following morning to remove the boards, the feather-bed rose up in her face, for the box was full of water. Hastily replacing the boards and drawing the bedstead over them, she hurried to her parents' room.

"Father," she cried, "you must go, for it is not safe for you to be here any longer. The hole is flooded, and even if we baled the water out, it would give you your death of rheumatism if you had to slip into it in a hurry."

Sir Patrick looked grave at the news. " Aweel, if that is so," he said, after a moment's silence, " I think it is time that we all sought refuge in the Low Countries. Since I have suffered in the Reformed cause, I can well claim the protection of the Prince of Orange. My lands may be forfeit, at least for a time, but I believe I shall live to return and have them restored to me ; and for the present, though I may be counted a dead man, they will be obliged to give thee," turning to his wife, "a jointure, as if thou wert my widow, and on that we must manage to subsist until better times come."

These words proved a prophecy ! For that very night Sir Patrick crept out of a window and stole away, like a thief in the night, from his family home. By keeping to unfrequented paths on the Lammermuir Hills he gained the Border, and in time reached London, whence he crossed to Holland, and obtaining, as he had hoped, the protection of the Prince of Orange, he settled at Utrecht, where his wife and family joined him in September, 1684.

His estates were confiscated and given to Lord Seaforth, and for nearly four years Lady Hume's slender jointure of a hundred and fifty pounds had to provide lodging, food, and clothing for her family. Needless to say they could afford little outside help.

So Lady Hume and her daughters did the housework, while Sir Patrick taught the younger children, and in the evenings Grizel, who was always the stand-by of the family, mended the children's clothes, and washed and ironed her brother Patrick's cravat and cuffs, so that he might look as well dressed as his richer companions.

We wonder, looking back at the story, if she washed and ironed another young soldier's cravat and cuffs as well !

For her father's friend, George Baillie of Jerviswood, had never left the Tolbooth in Edinburgh, except to walk to the scaffold, and his son, a younger George, had also fled to Holland, and along with young Patrick Hume, our heroine's elder brother, had enlisted in the Prince of Orange's guards.

It may well have been so, for Grizel and George Baillie were great friends, and doubtless it lightened her labours to know he was near. And when at the Revolution in 1688 William of Orange went to reign in England, and Sir Patrick's lands were restored to him, and they all went back to Berwickshire—Sir Patrick with the new title of Lord Polwarth—Grizel did not stay very long at Redbraes, but went over to Jerviswood, there to reign as a happy wife and mother for wellnigh sixty years.

XIII

THE COBBLER OF STONEYWOOD

THE ribbon was white once, little Dorothy, and thy great-grandfather pinned it on my breast when he bade my mother and me good-bye on the doorstep of Stoneywood, far away in Aberdeenshire, and rode off to follow his Prince in his desperate effort to regain his father's crown.

It was in the summer of 1745, the year when Prince Charlie landed in Scotland and raised his standard. I was but a lassie of fifteen at the time, but I had been brought up loyal to the Stewarts, and had been taught to look upon the Princes of the House of Hanover as aliens and usurpers. Aye, and I think so still, little woman, although I have lived here in England under their rule for nigh on sixty years, and people smile at what they call my "old-fashioned fancies" when I pass my glass of port over the water-bottle, when the toast of the King is given. They would not have smiled sixty years ago, when the memory of the '45 was still fresh in their minds, but would have been fain to make me stand my trial as a traitor; but now they seem to think that all risk of another rising is past, so they let me alone, and humour me as if I were a child, and tell me that German George and his descendants are too firmly seated on the British throne to be displaced by any Pretender.

Which always makes my blood boil, child, old and thin as it is, because it is he whom they call his Majesty George III. who is the Pretender, and who sits on a throne that belongs of right to another man.

But there, child, I did not mean to frighten thee with my vehemence. 'Tis a question over which even thy grandfather and I could never agree, seeing 'twas the one and only bone of contention between us. And 'twas no wonder, seeing that he was an Englishman and a Hanoverian, while I was Highland born and bred, being the daughter of a Jacobite laird.

But, for the great love we bore one another, we agreed to differ, so that there was never dissension nor quarrelling between us, as there otherwise might have been.

But I am wandering away from my story, little Dorothy, and from the knot of white ribbon which hath made thee so curious.

Well, as I say, my father rode away to follow Prince Charlie, with all the able-bodied men who lived in the cottages round Stoneywood at his back, and attended by John Gunn, who had always acted as his body-servant, as well as being the factotum of the whole household. My father and he once went to London in their young days, but that belongs not to my tale at present; I must tell thee about that another day.

There were no men left on the estate at all, save an old gamekeeper or two, who had been in my grandfather's service, and were therefore too old to go, and Robbie Grant, the cobbler, who lived down in a cottage by the side of the Don, who had to stay at home also, much against his will, for he was so crippled by rheumatism, caused, maybe, by the mists that hung about the river in the winter, that he could not march with the rest.

This was no loss to my mother and me, for Robbie was a cheery man, whose head seemed filled with yarns and tales of divers sorts, and many a walk did we take to his cottage, and many an hour did we spend with him in the dark winter afternoons, when our spirits were low and our hearts heavy.

For it was but dreary work for two lone women (for though I was but a child when all was said and done, I thought myself a woman) to be left to themselves through a long Scottish winter, with nobody to keep them company save a handful of serving-wenches and two little bairns. For my little brother and sister, who were twins, had been born when I was a big lass of eight years old.

So they were little running things of seven at the time of which I speak, and, although they amused us with their prattle, they were no real company to my mother and me.

The long winter went slowly by, and the next summer came on. At times we heard news of my father and the Prince. At first they were in the Highlands, and then in Edinburgh, where the Prince was proclaimed King at the Market Cross. Then came word of the glorious victory at Prestonpans; then, after long months had passed, we heard of the advance into England, by Preston and Derby, and hopes ran high. Then came more months of weary waiting, during which we heard nothing for certain, nothing but evil rumours of a retreat which had been passed from mouth to mouth, and at which our hearts sank, although we said to one another with bold faces that we would yield them no belief.

And then, at long and weary last, when the winter was gone and the spring nigh upon us, the blow fell.

It was towards the end of April, and I had taken the twins out to the green behind the house, where the linen was bleached and the clothes dried on washing-days, to have a game of ball with them before they went to bed. The ball had rolled into the root of an old thorn hedge, and Alison was seeking for it, and I was amusing myself meanwhile by gathering a little bunch of the bonny yellow aconite which grew on either side of the little path that led through the wood in the direction of Robbie Clark's cottage.

All at once I saw John Gunn standing back among the trees, and at sight of him the cold sweat broke over my face, and my legs trembled as though I had suddenly been seized with the ague.

For it was not the John Gunn who had ridden away with my father ten months ago, with his strong shoulders squared and a smile on his face, as if he were setting out to conquer the world, but an old, broken man, or so it seemed to me then, with white face, sunken cheeks, great hollow eyes, a beard which had not seen a razor for a month, and an arm in a dirty, blood-stained sling.

"John!" I cried, running up to him, "oh, John, what hath befallen, and where are my father and the rest of the men?"

"Disaster hath befallen, Mistress Christian," said John bluntly, "disaster dire and dread. The Prince's army met the Duke of Cumberland's

levies on Culloden Moor two days ago, and our
men went down before them like ill-rooted fir
trees in a winter's storm. Thy father came out
of it safely, however, and hath taken to the hills.
But as for the men, I fear me most of them have
fallen—most of them, that is, that were spared to
return from England."

"But, John, hath the Prince's army lost the
day? I thought it was always victorious," I
gasped, aghast at this confirmation of the fears
that had been pressing in on us as the long months
went by.

"It hath been beaten this time, Mistress
Christian," said John Gunn grimly and slowly,
"and I fear me it will be many a long day ere
it rally again. But see, there are the bairns coming
to look for thee. Get them out of the way like
a sensible lass, ere they catch sight of me in this
guise. I have words to speak which are for the
mistress's ear alone, and I have no desire to have
all the silly serving-wenches screeching and wailing
round us as though the last day had come. We
may weather the storm yet, so it is as well to keep
as quiet a sough* as may be."

Girl as I was, I saw that there was sense in what
he said, so, saying hastily that I would tell my
mother where he was, I retraced my steps to

* Keep as quiet a sough, to keep as quiet.

where the twins, who had by this time found the ball, were standing hand in hand, peering up the wood rather timidly. For they had not recognized John Gunn, and had a wholesome dread of strangers.

For the next quarter of an hour I kept up such a vigorous game with them that by the end of it they were glad to follow me indoors to the nursery, where I left them in the charge of Mirren, the lassie whom my mother kept to scrub the pans in the kitchen in the morning and help old Janet with the twins in the afternoon.

Then I went slowly along to my mother's room, where I found her at her writing-table in the west window, casting up accounts, the rays of the setting sun lighting up her bonny hair.

For your great-grandmother was by-ordinar handsome, little Dorothy, tall and supple as a lath, with curly auburn hair, and one of the sweetest faces that it hath been my lot to see.

" Are you alone, Christian ?" she asked, looking up from her counting. " Where are Archie and Alison ?" For the twins were always wont to spend an hour with her before they went to bed.

" I left them with Mirren," I replied, " for I needed to speak with thee alone." And then I told her my story, breaking into sobs as I did so, for the news that John Gunn had brought was too dreadful.

My mother's face grew white as she listened, but her courage did not fail her as mine had done, although it was only when I was a woman grown that I realized fully all that the baneful tidings meant to her.

Nay, rather, she did everything in her power to hearten me, by putting her arms round me and kissing my forehead, and praising me to my face (a thing she was little wont to do), telling me that I had acted with great discretion, and that it strengthened her heart to know that in the hard days that might be in front of us she could trust to me being a help and comfort.

Then she bade me find Janet and tell her that she would fain speak with her, and then slip out into the wood to John Gunn and bring him in at the front door, so that no one should have the chance of seeing him.

Drying my tears, I ran off to do my errands, so uplifted by her words that I almost forgot the fight on Culloden Moor or the ill news about my father.

I found our trusty servant waiting for me in the plantation, sitting half asleep on the stump of a tree, and, as it was now the gloaming, we had no difficulty in getting in at the front door unobserved, and upstairs to my mother's room.

She cried out with pity when she saw John's unsteady gait and white face, and would not let him utter a word till Janet, who was waiting beside her, went to the pantry and brought him a glass of wine and the piece of venison pasty which had been left from our dinner.

These my mother set before him with her own hands, and from the way he devoured the pasty one would have thought he had not tasted food for days, which, indeed, as we learned later, he had hardly done.

He certainly seemed better when he had finished, for the pinched look had left his face, and he was more like the great, good-natured giant whom the twins and I had always counted on to help us in any ploy or adventure that we might have on hand.

Then with a " by your leave, my Leddy," he pulled his chair nearer to the blazing fire, and while we three women crowded round him, he told us the story of all that had befallen him since he rode off with my father nearly a year before.

Of the high hopes at first, and the grand doings in Edinburgh. The triumph at Prestonpans, and the march into England. Then the unlooked-for check at Derby, the retreat on Preston and Carlisle, during which many of our fine lads had been lost. Then the final rally in the north, and the struggle on the bleak moor of Culloden, which had ended so disastrously.

" The master and I fought side by side," he said, " and at the end of it we were both unhurt, save for this gash that was left on my shoulder by an English broadsword. 'Tis all so vague and confused I can scarce tell thee what befell, save that we stood together, and it seemed to me that we were for hours in the thickest of the fight. At last the battle seemed to roll away from us, and we were left alone save for the dead and dying, and we saw in front of us—God pity that I should live to tell it !—our ranks all broken, and the men flying like partridges before our foes. So there seemed nothing left to be done but to think of ourselves and how we could best get to the hills in safety.

" We crept up a burnside for a mile or two, and then, coming to a little glen all covered with hazels and rowans, we lay beneath a crag till night fell, when we could escape under cover of the darkness.

" From the first the master determined to bide among the hills, and not to attempt to return to Stoneywood. He knows full well that a price will be set on his head, and that they will seek for him here. So his plan is to use one of the hiding-places that he and some of the other leaders know of, and maybe, if he can manage it, fly the country altogether till the fray goes by.

" Of course, I expected to share his wanderings, for we have never been long parted, since we were laddies together, and I was sore angered and disappointed when he bade me come home, as he thought all the hue and cry would be for him, an' little heed would be paid to the like o' me.

" But the anger died in my heart, and I was content to do his bidding, when he laid his hand on my shoulder and said, ' John, my man, fain would I have thee with me, but I must think o' my wife and bairns. Thou canst do more for them, and more for me, if thou art at Stoneywood, and wherever I am, or wherever I may chance to be, my heart will be lighter and my courage higher, if I know that they have a man's strong arm to protect them, whatever befall.'

" So we parted at daybreak, and here I am, mistress, to do the best I can for thee, till my master comes home again."

" And right glad I am to see thee, John," replied my mother, taking his great hand in her slim white one. For she knew that his heart was sore, and anxious too, in case she should think he had lightly deserted my father.

Then she ordered me to seek my supper for myself and get off to bed, while Janet and she washed and dressed John's wound and bound it up again; and when I rose next morning I found him going about his work as usual, only that he wore his left arm in a sling, and spoke more gruffly than was his wont to the serving-wenches, who would have left their work, if they had dared, to hang round him and question him.

A week passed by, and we were getting somewhat accustomed to the new state of things, for we had heard nothing to make us think that my father had been taken, and we had good hope that by now he had succeeded in reaching the coast unobserved and getting on board some boat bound for France or the Low Countries, when all at once these hopes were dashed to the ground.

For late one evening, when the bairns were in bed, and my mother and I were sitting cantily by the fireside, we heard a great trampling of horses' hoofs in the courtyard, and, looking out, we saw some ten or twelve dragoons in the hated uniform worn by the forces of the Duke of Cumberland, led by a smooth-faced young officer, who had leaped from his horse and was now kicking

at the great door with clatter enough to bring
the house down.

The noisy summons was answered by John
Gunn, and a few minutes later the stranger was
ushered into our presence.

He was a good-looking youth, though he came
in the guise of an enemy. "Madam," he said,
and his voice was grave and courteous, "I am
sorry to disturb you and your household, but
I have a warrant from the Duke of Cumberland
which bids me search the mansion house of Stoneywood in order to see that there are no traitors
lurking therein. Also it contains instructions to
the effect that I and my men are to be billeted
here, to preserve law and order in the district
and to uphold the rightful authority of the King."

"In plain words you are here to watch for
my husband," said my mother, rising to her feet,
her lips white, but showing no other signs of
emotion.

"These are my instructions, madam," replied
the officer. "And believe me, I have no wish
to cause you more trouble than is absolutely
necessary. My name is Maurice de Trafford,
here is my commission from the Duke." He pulled
a paper from his pocket, and would have handed
it to her, but she waved it away with a little
gesture of contempt.

"I have no doubt that you are acting within your rights, sir," she said, "and the house is open for your inspection. As to the quartering of your men, my servant John Gunn will see to that; all that I ask of you is, that my children and I may be left in peace. If there is anything that you wish brought to my ears, you will find John Gunn a trustworthy messenger."

It seemed to me that the young man would fain have added something to what he had already said, but my mother's look was so cold and distant that, after glancing at her uncertainly for a moment, he took his dismissal and with a stately bow left the room.

"Run to Janet, and tell her to take the bairns from their beds and bring them here," said my mother, as soon as the door had closed behind him. "I will not have them scared out of their wits for any Duke of Cumberland and his minions. Nay, child, do not look so ghostlike," she added, for now that the stranger was gone, my knees had been seized with a great shaking, so that I was fain to sit down. "They may search the house from top to bottom if they will, they will not find their quarry here."

"But if they remain here, Mother," I whispered, "and my father happened to come home! He will walk right into their arms, as a rat into a trap."

" Heaven forfend !" cried my mother, and her eyes grew troubled. But she bravely strove to put such thoughts away from herself and me, by telling me " not to sup sorrow with a long spoon," but to run and do her bidding, before the men, who were already ransacking the rooms on the ground floor, could come up the stairs and enter our sleeping apartments.

They must have had a firm belief that my father was hidden somewhere in the house, for they searched it from garret to cellar, even coming into the room where we sat cowering round the fire, my mother and Janet each with a sleeping bairn on her knee. How the twins could sleep through the racket, I know not, for those men knocked on the walls and stamped with all their might on the floor, to discover by the sound if there was any secret hiding-place behind or beneath. They even tore down the great picture of my father which hung above the chimney-piece, in order that they might see if there was no secret door or panel in the wall behind it.

'Twas midnight ere they had finished their search and had retired downstairs to the great hall, which they intended to use, so John Gunn told us, as their sleeping quarters, while their officer took possession of the little parlour which adjoined it, and which had always been used by my father as his writing-room and office.

Next morning they rode out to search the woods and policies, leaving two of their number behind them to guard the house, and to keep watch, so we supposed, in case my father, thinking that all danger was past, returned. Day after day they kept to this order of things, two soldiers remaining in the house, keeping a sharp look-out on all who came and went, while the rest rode away in the morning, on what behest we could too well guess, and only returned at nightfall, when it grew too dark to carry on their cruel quest. We never crossed a word with them, for my mother had given strict orders that all the women-folk in the house were to bide upstairs, our very food being cooked in a disused bedroom.

John Gunn, whose wound was by this time wellnigh healed, fetched and carried food and fuel, and kept watch and ward over the twins and myself when, twice a day, we went out to take an airing on the hillside or down by the river.

Ah me! it was a dreary time, little Dorothy, and though more than sixty years have passed since then, I can still remember the sickness that came over me when I heard the trampling of the horses' hoofs as the riders rode home in the gloaming, and see in fancy my mother's white, set face, as she strained her eyes to discover if they came alone, or if they had brought my father with them. When she saw they had come alone, she would light the lamp, and call us to supper with cheerful haste, as though some burden were lifted off her; but by the next morning it had fallen again, and weighed heavier and heavier as it grew towards nightfall.

I remember how, lassie though I was, I wondered how long it could go on without her heart breaking, and how I often felt as if I needs must go to the English captain myself and beg of him to go away.

And, in good sooth, at last I did so, although, had I been older, I would have known that such a request was useless, and that the granting of it was altogether out of Maurice de Trafford's power.

But in after days he told me that the first time he paid any heed to the fact that there was a young maiden in the house was when I ran out from behind a whinbush on the hillside, as he was riding by one day, and, catching hold of his bridle-rein, cried out in a voice so full of despair that it went straight to his heart, " Oh, if you have any pity in you, will you not go away? My father never did you any harm, and you are just breaking my mother's heart."

I remember how his horse would have reared in the air at the sight of my white gown, and maybe come down on the top of me, had its rider not jumped to the ground and held it tight by the head, the while he looked down at me with a grave but kindly look on his face.

" I wish I could, little one," he said gently, " I wish I could, but it is impossible. When thou art older, thou wilt find that sometimes duty will keep thee where thou wouldst not willingly stay."

Then he lifted his plumed hat to me, as if I were woman grown, and, swinging himself into his saddle again, rode quickly off, while I ran back to the house, disappointed and shamed that my pleading had met with so little success, and scared at the thought of what my mother would say if it ever came to her ears that I had spoken to the enemy.

It must have been but a couple of days after this that we noticed one morning when the men rode out that their captain was not at their head, and later on we learned from John Gunn that the young man had kept his bed and seemed feverish and unwell. It had poured with rain all the day before, and doubtless he had got wet through and had caught a chill in consequence. " Serve him right," cried Janet with a chuckle; " it will teach him not to be so fond of our hilltops in wet weather." And my mother, although she said nothing, did not look sorry either.

But it seemed no common cold that the captain had caught, but a high fever, which caused pains in all his bones. And as the days went on these pains, so John Gunn reported, grew sharper and sharper, until at last they became so cruel that it seemed as if they had their victim on the rack.

" Serve him right," cried Janet again. " What of our poor men, the master among them, who maybe are lying in caves, or out in the open amongst the peat-hags, with their bones aching also, and not the chance of a bed to lie in."

But I noticed that my mother did not answer, but went about looking even graver than was her wont; and that night, before the bairns went to bed, she gathered us round her, and read the story out of the Good Book, about the man who owed the big debt to his master, and his master let him off, and who went straight away and put a poor man into prison who only owed him a little sum of money. I never liked that story, and I wondered why my mother read it that night, or why old Janet went out of the room with a swish of her petticoat tails and her head carried high in the air when she took the bairns to bed.

I understood it better in the morning, for when

I came into my mother's room for my breakfast, after having fed the hens, and helped the twins to gather a handful of dandelions for their rabbits, I found Janet and her having an argument, which was not an ordinary thing.

"Nay, Janet," said my mother as I entered, "'tis our duty to do our best to save his life, if so be he is in as grievous a case as John Gunn feareth. Enemy though he be, he is at best little more than a boy, and I could never again crave mercy from God for me and mine, were I to let him lie under my roof sick unto death without doing all in my power to save him."

"Aweel, my Leddy, if ye feel like that, ye maun just have your way," replied Janet, twirling the corner of her checked apron between her fingers as she spoke; "but it seems to me there is no call for us to fash our head about a recreant English-man who has taken his oath to serve a foreign King, and who would deliver up the master to-morrow to be hanged and quartered, if he could but lay hands on him.

My mother had been looking out of the window, but she turned sharply to our old nurse, who had been her nurse as well, and her face was white and quivering. "An you love me, Janet, do not say such things," she exclaimed; "for if you do, my courage will fail, and my heart will die within me, and I shall never have the strength to thole this weary time of waiting."

" 'Deed, an' it's me that should be ashamed of myself," said Janet in a softer voice, " for I should hae learned better than tae be telling ye to render evil for evil. But I just canna bide the sight o' thae English loons, an' that is the truth, mistress. But if it is your pleasure that this young man should be nursed, nursed he shall be. For I would do anything in the wide world for you an' the bairns."

" I know that, Janet, and right heartily I thank you," replied my mother. " So, like the good-hearted woman that thou art, wilt thou see after breakfast that the guest-chamber is set in order, and a warming-pan of glowing embers put in the bed. For if, as John Gunn thinks, along with the fever, the lad is crippled with rheumatism, 'twill do him more harm than good, if we put him between cold sheets. And when thou hast done that, Janet, make a good big basin of Malvoisie whey. 'Tis both cooling and nourishing, and no one can make it as thou dost. Thou knowest thou hast told me ofttimes, when I was a little lass just two years older than Alison, and was so distraught with fever that my life was despaired of, thou coaxedst me to drink a cupful, after which I fell into the deep sleep which the doctors say saved my life."

Janet left the room with a smile on her face. My mother knew how to manage the old woman, and knew also that she was such a skilful nurse that, if once she were thoroughly interested in her patient, she would soon forget whether he were friend or foe.

And so it proved. For many days after he was carried up into the guest-chamber in the west turret, Maurice de Trafford's life hung in the balance, and Janet, her heart softening towards him in his helplessness, nursed him as if he had been one of the family, and almost forgot, in her anxiety for his welfare, Alison and Archie, who, my mother's time also being much occupied with the sick man, were left almost entirely to my care.

At last, however, he took the turn, and began to mend, and well I remember the first evening that he was able to leave his room, and, in order that " it might be aired," as Janet put it, crawled along, leaning on her arm, to my mother's sitting-room, looking so like a ghost that the bairns, who were listening to a fairy tale that I was telling them, thought that he was a real " draiglin hoglin," there being such a creature in my story, and shrieked and ran and hid their little faces in the folds of Janet's gown.

They got accustomed to his presence in the

sitting-room, however, for, though it was now the end of May, the days were cold and wet, and my mother, who had been taken with the young man's gentle, mild-mannered ways, and his deep and heartfelt gratitude for all that had been done for him, would not hear of his going back to his quarters in the great draughty hall, but insisted that he should remain upstairs till his strength came back and the weather had grown warmer.

Nor did she lose anything by her kindness, and one could not blame her if she recognized this, for although the captain had some of the dragoons to speak to him every day, and the men rode forth as usual, they seemed to have lost their keenness for the quest, and returned home sooner at night, to sit over the fire, so John Gunn reported, and sing songs, or gamble for what small money they had.

And so Captain Maurice, as we came to call him, spent many an hour on the low settle beside the fire, telling the bairns tales of the old red-tiled manor house near the city of Lincoln, which was his home, and of his mother and his two little sisters, one of whom had died the year before, and who had been, he sometimes said, looking across the hearth to where I sat, maiden-like, on my stool beside my mother, wondrous like me.

Then he would speak of the great Cathedral on Lincoln Hill, which thou knowest so well, little Dorothy, with its carven tower and Angel Choir, and tell how his mother went to service there on the greater Festivals, and my mother, who had always clung to the Church and its Liturgy, howbeit it could only be read in private, wellnigh forgot he was an Englishman and a Hanoverian, in her interest in his talk.

Nevertheless, we all felt as if a load were lifted from the house, when, the weather having improved, and Captain Maurice having taken to riding again, he came hurrying up the stairs one June morning with a folded paper in his hand.

" I bring what must be good news to you, madam," he said; " I am recalled to Edinburgh, with my dragoons."

My mother was of too truthful a nature not to let her relief be clearly written on her face. Yet it was almost like parting with a friend when we shook hands with the young Englishman on the doorstep next morning, and watched him ride away at the head of his men.

" I am sure Captain Maurice is half for the Prince, Mother," I said, " for he hath taken away the half of my knot of white ribbon with him. It fell off, and he picked it up and asked me if he might part it in two, and carry one part of it with him, to let his little sister Margery see what the Jacobite maidens wore."

" If they find that in his possession, they'll shoot him as a traitor," cried Janet anxiously, as if the prospect did not please her (and yet a few weeks before she would have shot him gladly with her own hands). " 'Tis not safe for a Hanoverian to carry the White Cockade."

" 'Tis not exactly the White Cockade," replied my mother with a queer look on her face, half sad, half diverted. " 'Tis only part of Christian's knot of ribbon, and none too clean. Let us hope that Mistress Margery de Trafford will be much edified by the sight of it. But come, bairns, let us go and pick a posy of primroses, and feel that Stoneywood is our very own again."

A week had not passed ere we found ourselves in the midst of another great excitement. At least my mother, Janet, John Gunn, and myself found ourselves in it, for it was too serious and anxious an affair to let any of the other servants get knowledge of it.

My father came home ! Quite suddenly and unexpectedly one night in the gloaming, just as John Gunn had come, and nearly scared my mother and me out of our wits, by walking straight upstairs and into the sitting-room as though the Rising had never been, and he was as safe as in time of peace. He had heard that the English soldiers had gone away home, he told us, and he knew he had nothing to fear from his own people.

But my mother and I knew better, for we had heard of one and another who had been betrayed by a thoughtless word, spoken, mayhap, by some young servant, who had been won over by the soft speech of the English, and who had given away secrets that they would have bitten their tongues out rather than betray, without being aware that they had done so.

So we persuaded him, much against his will, to hide in the little cupboard that opened off the sitting-room until everything was quiet and the household had gone to bed. Then we brought him food and water and clean clothes, of which he stood much in need, for those he wore were tattered and mud-stained. When he was warmed and refreshed, we gathered round the fire, having first blown out the candles, in case any busybody wandering about outside should note the unwonted hour at which we had lights burning.

We listened while he told us what he had been doing all these weeks : how he had lain hidden for most of the time in a cave high up among the mountains, and how a shepherd's wife, whose husband had also got safely away from

Culloden field, had kept him well supplied with milk and bannocks.

He had felt it cold at nights, and the time had been very wearisome, as he dare not venture out in the daylight, nor, for that part of it, in the moonlight either, so that it was only on very dark or stormy nights that he got any fresh air at all.

Then when news had reached the lonely spot that the English soldiers who had been scouring the country for the leaders of the Rising had been recalled to the south, he had bidden farewell to his kind friends and turned his face in the direction of home.

As was natural, he had heard little or nothing of what was going on while he lay in his hiding-place, and his look grew grave while my mother recounted to him the dreadful things that had happened to some of our friends : how some of them had been shot down or hanged, without a hearing being granted them, some carried off to London to stand their trial, and some shipped to the plantations.

" Maybe 'tis as well that all the world should not know that I have returned," he said at last ; " but if I keep quietly to the house and grounds, and warn our people to keep watch over their tongues, there will not, surely, be much risk."

" 'Deed, master, it wouldna be safe at all,"
broke in John Gunn bluntly. "Ye just canna
be allowed to trust your life to all and sundry.
Some of the lads and lassies are sensible enough,
but others are as thoughtless as can be, and at
this time it is hard to judge who may or may
not be a spy and a traitor, and be in the pay of
the enemy. No, 'tis a pity but you had bidden
where you were for another month or two, if ye
couldna manage to get safely to the coast. But
seeing that ye are here, we must find some other
hiding-place for ye—some place that no one
knows save us four that are listening to ye just
now."

The words were roughly, almost rudely, spoken;
but one had only to see the anxiety that was
clearly written on John Gunn's countenance to
know that it was his heartfelt love for my father
that had forced him to speak as he did.

" Do you not think he would be safe if he
stayed in the house, John, and slipped into this
closet when any of the other servants came this
way?" asked my mother, who, now that she
had got my father, was loath to part with him
again. " We could keep an extra cup and plate
in the press, and no one need know that he shared
our meals."

" It just wouldna do at all, mistress," replied

John emphatically. "The soldiers have gone south, but I just heard this morning that they had gone no further than Perth. Who knows but that their going was just a trick to deceive people, and that they may not return to search our houses when they think the owners have had time to get back, and when we least expect them? Na, na; the master may bide here to-night, but he must find other quarters the morn."

But where could he go? That was the question which we discussed and debated till the small hours of the morning, without coming to any decision.

At last, through sheer weariness, we gave it up, and the talk drifted back to my father's doings as he lay hidden among the hills.

"You should have learned to knit, Father," I said, squeezing his hand between mine, just to be sure that he was really beside me, and that it was not a dream.

"I did try, Christian," he answered, returning the squeeze with so much vigour that I was fain to cry out, "but it was not a success. My fingers were too big and clumsy. I just wasted the guidwife's wool, and had nothing to show for it. But one thing I could do, thanks to the hours I spent on rainy days in Robbie Grant's cottage, I could cobble the bairns' shoon."

18

At these words John Gunn sprang to his feet in such a hurry that we all looked at him in amazement.

" I have it," he cried, bringing his big clenched fist down on the mantelpiece, over which my father's portrait once more hung. " It's to Robbie Grant's cottage that ye'll go again. He can make a hidey-hole in the wall ahint his big box bed, where ye can sleep at nights. I can carry plenty blankets down without anybody being a whit the wiser. And in the daytime ye can sit and cobble in the back room. No hereabout body needs ken ye are there at all. There is no need for Robbie to let his customers ben the hoose, and if sae be it ever came to be searched, he can introduce ye to the searchers as his prentice. Maybe ye look a bittie old for the part, but in those troublous times folk must understand that it's none so easy to get lads for prentices."

So the matter was settled, for we all knew that Robbie Grant was as true as steel, and the plan seemed the best that could be thought of. For Robbie's cottage stood by itself, quite hidden by the trees, and it did not seem likely, even if the soldiers came back to search the big house, that they would ever remember its existence.

So, as dawn was now breaking, John Gunn

went off then and there to waken Robbie and arrange matters with him, and before the workaday world was astir, my father was settled in his new quarters, where, as we afterwards heard, he spent the whole day and the next night sleeping off his weariness in a comfortable bed which had been hastily prepared for him in the hidey-hole by his two faithful friends.

Once he was properly rested, he used to get up through the day and sit in Robbie's little back room, which, luckily, was but ill-lighted and dark, wiling away the time as best he could, doing any little bits of cobbling that Robbie could trust him with, even learning more of the craft, till, at the end of a month, Robbie declared he was as good a cobbler as himself.

We saw little of him, as it was not thought advisable for us to be seen going often to the cottage; but you may be sure that, in those weeks, we were quick to notice any worn bit on our shoes that would be the better of a patch. And there was footgear of the bairns, that had been cast aside as useless, that was sought out again and taken down to the cobbler to see what he could make of it.

But as a rule it was John Gunn who did the fetching and carrying, slipping out at night, when everyone had gone to bed, with a basketful of food with which to replenish Robbie's larder, and bringing back my father's clothes when they needed to be washed or mended, which offices my mother and Janet performed by lamplight, or in the early morning when the house was still.

So another six weeks went by, and although John Gunn always shook his head when we spoke of it, we womenfolk were beginning to wonder if my father could not come boldly out and resume his life at home, when one morning the bairns came rushing into the house, full of excitement, little knowing what tidings of evil they brought with them.

" The soldiers are back again, Mother," cried Archie, " the soldiers, the bonny soldiers ! There is one sitting on his horse at the gate, and another on the green at the back, and the rest of them are hunting among the straw in the byre and the hen-house. I think they are looking for eggs."

" There are only seven of them there, for I counted," said Alison, in her slow, deliberate way. " The rest were riding off with Captain de Trafford down the brae to Robbie Grant's."

My mother looked at me over the twins' heads, with a face like death. And if ever I saw anguish in mortal eyes, I saw it then.

" Bide with Janet, bairns," she said; " Christian and I have some work to do in the guest-chamber."

In silence I followed her up to the pleasant, sunny room in the western turret, where, a few months before, the man who had now returned to make our home desolate had been nursed and succoured. It must have been a bitter moment for my mother, and as for me, little Dorothy, my heart was as heavy as lead.

For although I would have died rather than confess it, I had been weaving all sorts of romances in my mind in which Maurice de Trafford had figured as a peerless young knight, who had come to see the error of his ways, and forsworn the service of George of Hanover to take arms in the cause of our own Prince Charlie.

And here were my romances swept away at one blow, and the naked truth presented to me that, although the young knight of my dreams had returned, it was still in the guise of an enemy, who this time could not fail, it seemed to me, to catch my father and lead him to his death. And to my mother, also, the turn that things had taken seemed hopeless.

" Oh, Christian," she moaned, drawing me down beside her in the window-seat in the great window of the guest-chamber, which overlooked the path that led to Robbie Grant's cottage, " what fools we have been ! We have had him undisturbed all these weeks, and notwithstanding John Gunn's warnings, we have taken the matter so lightly that we believed all danger was past. Perchance if we had but seen to it, we might have got him safely away to Denmark or Flanders in an Aberdeen fishing ketch. And 'twas I, selfish woman that I am, who did it. I wanted to feel that he was near us—and I took no steps. And now, if they have eyes in their heads, they will find him, and they will take his life as a traitor, my bonny man !"

" Oh, Mother, wheesht !" I entreated, for her speech was so wild that it frightened me. " Perhaps Robbie would see them coming, and get Father into the hidey-hole, and push the box bed back into its place."

" And do you think the soldiers would let it bide there ?" cried my mother shrilly. "Not they ! They will nose and hunt about, until they find their prey and drag him out."

Then she was silent, straining her eyes against the glass for the first sight of her husband being brought up the path as a prisoner, bound and helpless. Never to the end of my life, little Dorothy, will I forget the misery of that quarter of an hour.

Even now I can hardly tell thee of the throb of

relief that went through my body as a horse's head appeared at the edge of the wood, then another, and another, and the whole of the little band of men appeared with Maurice de Trafford at their head, and I saw that they were riding alone. There was no prisoner in their midst.

It was as if my blood had been frozen for a space, but was now set flowing again.

" He is not there, Mother," I whispered, and then all of a sudden I began to shake, and would speedily have burst out crying, had not my mother taken me by the shoulders and spoken clearly and sharply.

" Pull thyself together, Christian, and if ever thou wert a woman, be one now," she said. " They will search this house next, and maybe take up their abode here to watch for thy father, as they did before; and we must not let them suspect, by word or look, that any of us have seen him, or that he is in the neighbourhood.

" See, the captain hath caught sight of us, and is saluting. Wave thy kerchief to him, then we'll get the bairns and go down to the hall to meet him. He must not think that we are at all put about at his coming." So we made a brave show on the doorstep when the riders drew up and the captain jumped from his horse and bent low over my mother's hand ; for the bairns were capering about, delighted at his coming, and I myself, now that the danger seemed over for the present, felt wondrous glad to see Captain Maurice's pleasant face again. This may seem a curious thing to say, but it is the truth ; and I can only explain it by the fact that there was such a cheery ring in his voice as he greeted my mother, that somehow I felt that he knew that he could work us no harm, and was relieved by the knowledge.

But, although the sound of his voice was cheerful, his words were brusque and soldierly enough.

"We have returned, madam," he said, "but only for a passing visit. I have orders to search your house, as news hath reached my colonel in Perth that the Laird of Stoneywood hath returned home. Therefore it is my duty to ask you to give orders that no one attempt to leave the house, while my men are on guard at the doors. Indeed, it would be dangerous for them to do so. And I must ask you to retire to your sitting-room with Mistress Christian and the children, and to remain there while we do our duty."

"Certainly, sir," replied my mother, and she walked upstairs beside him with her head high, talking about this and that, and making enquiries as to his health, as though she had no other thought or concern in the world.

Nevertheless she looked strained and anxious as we waited, while the soldiers once more ransacked the house, as they had done on their first arrival. I knew what she was fearing. Somehow, somewhere, they might come on some trifle belonging to my father, that had been forgotten, and that would make them suspect that he had been to see us.

But nothing happened, and with a sigh of relief we listened to the heavy footsteps of the men as they tramped down the stairs again and out to the gravelled space before the door, where their horses were waiting in charge of two of their comrades.

Their captain followed them to give some orders, then turned and came to bid us farewell, accompanied by one of the soldiers who wore a different dress from the rest, and who, I suppose, was next to him in command. It seemed as if he did not wish to have any kind of private leave-taking.

" Adieu, madam," he said gravely. " Our search has proved fruitless, and we must hurry on to carry out our further orders. I myself am recalled to England, so it may be a long time ere we meet again. But, believe me, I shall not forget the kindness I have received at your hands. Adieu, Mistress Christian, adieu, Archie and Alison. I trust your lots may be cast in more peaceful times." And with a stiff bow, and never a handshake, he was gone.

I felt bewildered. Could it be that after all he was really disappointed that he was riding from Stoneywood empty-handed?

"He hath dropped his glove," cried Alison suddenly. "See here, in the dark behind the door. Look, Mother, what a bonny glove, all broidered with gold."

Just then hasty footsteps came flying up the stairs, and the captain ran in again, without so much as a knock. But it was the captain as he had been as an invalid, not the stiff and starched soldier who had bidden us farewell but a moment ago.

"I came for my glove, and for other things," he said. "To bid you all a real farewell, and to crave leave to return in happier times. And especially to say to you, madam"—and he glanced first at my mother, and then at the portrait of my father which looked down at her from the wall—"that in case my dragoons should be sent back to Stoneywood every now and then, *it would be advisable to have the cobbler's portrait removed, and buried perchance, for the present.*"

"I CAME FOR MY GLOVE AND FOR OTHER THINGS," HE SAID

Then, with a wave of his hand, he turned and ran downstairs again, and in a moment we saw him cantering down the path after his men, while Alison, still hugging the glove, which, after all, he had left behind, solemnly enquired what he meant, and my mother and I looked at one another with lumps in our throats and tears in our eyes.

"I wonder," at last she said softly, "if the unforgiving steward ever knew what he had missed."

*   *   *   *   *

As for the rest of the story, little Dorothy, there is not much to tell that you have not heard before.

You know how my father escaped to Denmark, and how my mother, Janet, myself and the bairns followed him, leaving John Gunn to look after our interests at Stoneywood. And it was when we were living in Aarhus, some four years after the events I have described, that one day Janet announced that a stranger was waiting below who would fain speak with Mr. Moir. And who should it be but Captain Maurice de Trafford, now raised to the rank of a colonel, who had come, as he told us, with one of his old merry laughs, to make the acquaintance of the cobbler of Stoneywood and to pay his respects to the rest of the family.

And somehow, away in that foreign land, the differences that divided us at home seemed to grow less, and the mere fact that the colonel spoke our common tongue made him like one of ourselves at once. So that we were little inclined to wrangle over politics, and much more given to talk of the days when the English stranger had lain, gathering his strength, on the settle by the fire, in my mother's sitting-room, and of the welcome he had received from his mother and sister when he went back to Lincolnshire.

So the old story of love, which, as long as there are men and maidens in the world, little Dorothy, will still be always new, ran on. Thy grandfather—for thou must have guessed it was he—found that mysterious " affairs " kept him in Aarhus, though what these affairs were no one ever heard. And as they did not seem to take up much of his time, he spent most of it with us. And at last one day on the ramparts, when he and I were alone, he pulled out this faded knot of ribbon, which he had kept all those years, and told me why he had kept it, and how his mother was dead, and his sister Margery married, and the old Lincolnshire manor, where we sit, sadly needing a mistress.

And when I, very shamefaced, and yet very proud withal, for I was scarce nineteen and had never before had a lover, went home and whispered the story of what he had said to my mother, while he was closeted with my father, I found to my astonishment that she was not unprepared to hear the tale.

And so it came about that, long before the time when my parents could return in safety to Stoneywood, I was the happy mistress of this peaceful old mansion, with a troop of little lads and lasses running at my foot, the eldest of whom is your father, little Dorothy. And as I see him coming across the fields now, let us draw the curtains and ring for the lamp. For men never like coming home to a dark house.

XIV

THE ROUT O' MOY

WOULD you like to hear how seven brave men and two bairns, scarce in their teens, routed fifteen hundred soldiers and sent them flying across the countryside as if the Evil One himself had been at their heels?

It was in February in the year 1745, and Prince Charlie, after his victory at Falkirk, had marched to the north, and, pressing on before his men, was enjoying a well-earned rest at Moy Castle, some sixteen miles from Inverness.

Queer as it may seem, the owner of the Castle, the Laird of Macintosh, was, outwardly at least, an upholder of the Government; but it looks as if he had been but half-hearted, for although he served, as in duty bound, under the Duke of Cumberland, he let his wife, who was all for Prince Charlie, do as she liked, and now in his absence she was sheltering the Prince, and most of the folk in the countryside knew it.

They also knew that it was likely that blood would be shed sooner or later, for the Earl of Loudoun, one of the Duke of Cumberland's

generals, lay in Inverness, with a small body of
fifteen hundred men. At first Lord Loudoun
did not know where the Prince was, but there is
aye somebody ready to sell a life for siller, and
by the middle of the month the secret had been
whispered in his ear that the man whom he was
seeking was at Moy, and that he was accompanied
by only one attendant.

So the Hanoverian commander laid his plans,
and decided that his men should march to the
Castle under cover of darkness and catch the
Prince like a rat in a hole.

This being so, he would have been a wise man
if he had kept his soldiers within bounds till they
were ready to set out, instead of letting them wander
all over the town. For, towards the darkening,
some of them forgathered in a tavern in the
narrow High Street, and, after quenching their
thirst with something stronger than water, began
to speak in whispers about the intended expedition.

One of them, more cautious than his neigh-
bours, tried to turn the conversation, but his
companions laughed at him. " We're all friends
here," they cried, " not a trace of a White Cockade
to be seen anywhere. Besides, the townsfolk are
too frightened to withstand us in any way. So
let's have another bottle of usquebaugh to drink

to the success of our venture and the downfall of the Pretender.

The barefooted, short-skirted lassie, with hair the colour of tow, who was serving them, brought another bottle of the fiery spirit and set it before them on the table. She was so little and so insignificant that no one noticed how the colour came and went on her cheek, and how tightly her lips were closed, and how bright her eyes.

As soon as the glasses began to go round, she slipped noiselessly out of the room and ran up the garret stairs.

" Lachlan," she whispered, opening a little wooden door, which led into a tiny room under the rafters, " Lachlan." A curly-headed boy, who stood under the skylight whittling a stick, looked up as she spoke.

" What is it, Jean? I thought you were serving the Sassenachs down below."

" So I was, for a mercy," answered his sister, " for what did I hear the rascals say? That their master has learned where the Prince is, and that the whole of them are marching to Moy Castle as soon as it is dark, to trap him and take him prisoner."

The boy's ruddy face grew white. For he and his sister had been brought up at Moy, where their father had been a shepherd until his death nine months before, and all their lives they had been taught that loyalty to the Stewarts was only next to loyalty to God Himself.

" What can we do, Jean?" he whispered. For he well knew that the innkeeper, a far-away relative with whom they now lived, did not hold the views they did, and would aid the Government troops as far as he dared.

" Do?" said Jean firmly. " Put on your coat and run to old Lady Macintosh's house as hard as your legs will carry you. Ask for madam herself, don't be put off by any of the servants, and tell her the whole story. She will know what to do, and maybe we may outwit these English scoundrels yet."

So saying she ran downstairs again, and was at her post at the dresser before the soldiers had time to miss her.

" Ye want to see her leddyship herself, do ye? Weel, I canna trouble her for a smatchet like you."

Lachlan raised a coaxing face to the cross old cook who had answered his rap, and at the same time lifted one of his bare feet out of the pool of water that came right up to the back door of the Dowager Lady Macintosh's town house, and planted it firmly on the doorstep.

" If I canna see her leddyship, at least let me

come in to the fire," he said. " It's a cold night, and the inn is so full of soldiers I had to sit in the garret."

Eelin signified by a nod of her head that the boy might come in. She had known his mother in the old days at Moy. Lachlan crept across the kitchen and sat down on the settle that stood near the door leading to the living-rooms.

Presently Morag Mackinnon, her ladyship's waiting-woman, opened the door and looked in, Apparently she was looking for Eelin, who had just carried a pot of refuse out to the dung-heap.

Lachlan jumped to his feet. Morag was years younger than Eelin, and had a much better temper.

" Morag," he said in a whisper, rising and slipping through the door, " Morag, I maun see old madam. 'Tis very particular, and there's no time to lose. 'Tis so particular, that if ye wunna tell her I'm here, I'll e'en have to gang right up to her parlour mysel'. For once I've got in here, I'm no going out without seeing her."

Morag's eyes were sharper than Eelin's, and she saw that under his brave manner the boy was trembling from head to foot, and that he had much ado to keep back his tears.

" All right, laddie," she replied, " if you're

so keen to see her leddyship, I'll gie ye your chance. I'm just carrying in her supper, and I'll tell her you're here."

Ten minutes later the boy, in his bare feet and tattered kilt, was pouring out his tale to a stately white-haired lady, who sat erect in a straight-backed chair before a blazing fire in a comfortable old-fashioned room hung with tapestry.

"You are a good and faithful lad, Lachlan," she said when he had finished, "and you showed your sense by coming direct to me, instead of crying the news all over the town. Sit down by that table there and eat your supper; Morag can bring me something else after you are gone. Eat your fill, laddie"— as the boy hesitated, embarrassed by the fine linen, sparkling glass, and solid silver of her ladyship's supper table— "for you'll need all your strength for the job that is before you. But you are both young and yauld,* and I warrant your legs will carry you to Moy faster than these Sassenachs can march. So you will bear a message from me to my daughter-in-law at the Castle, telling her that her visitor must begone at once, for Lord Loudoun and his troops are on the road to take him."

"Will ye give me a note to Lady Macintosh?

* Yauld, vigorous.

They might not let me see her," asked Lachlan anxiously, remembering his experience at the back door.

" No, I'll give you no note, then if Loudoun's men catch you, they can find nothing. But see, here is a blackcock's heckle," and she took a little tuft of feathers out of her workbox; " stick that in your bonnet, 'twill pass for your own. And if the porter at Moy questions you, give it to him and tell him to carry it to her ladyship. 'Twill win you an entry."

In twenty minutes Lachlan was off, let out at the front door by old madam herself. With a wisdom beyond his years, the boy walked soberly through the streets of the little town, even pretending to loiter now and then, so that no one might mark his hurry and wonder at it.

But when he was once in the open country he dropped his pretence of dawdling, and, pulling himself together, set out at a steady trot for his sixteen-mile run.

For six or seven miles all went well, and the boy was beginning to think that his task was going to be an easy one, and was allowing himself to walk occasionally, and even to sit down for a minute or two, just to get his breath and ease the ache which he was beginning to feel at the back of his legs.

But all of a sudden he drew in his breath sharply and stood motionless, listening. Yes, he could not be mistaken. From far down the road along which he had come a small body of soldiers were approaching. He could hear the clank of their harness, and their noisy laughter as they shouted to each other. It was plain they formed the vanguard of Lord Loudoun's detachment of troops.

Lachlan hesitated a moment. Should he pursue his way along the road? No! A man might be travelling like that at night on legitimate business, but not a boy of his age. He was sure to attract attention, and be stopped and questioned. Perhaps he might even be told to go back to Inverness. That was not to be thought of. So he must hide till the soldiers were past, then take to the hill. There was a track which he knew that would lead him to Moy, only it was some four miles longer than the road, and could he reach the Castle in time? What was it his father had always told him to do? "Set a stout heart to a stey* brae." Well, he would try to do that, and would trust that the stout heart would win.

The troopers were now gaining on him, in another minute they would be round the last corner and might see him on the road. There

* Stey, stiff.

was a ditch full of last year's bracken close by.
The boy lay down in it, clapped as flat as a
partridge, with his face pressed into the claggy
leaves.

There were only some twenty riders in the
advance party, but it seemed to Lachlan that
they took an eternity to pass. One of them
actually halted beside him, and picked a stone
out of his horse's shoe. But at last they disappeared round the corner of a fir wood. Then,
with a cautious look to see that they were really
out of sight, the boy rose to his feet and ran like
a hare up the hill.

"Please, your leddyship, but young Lachlan
Maclean—his father herded the outbye hirsel',
if ye mind—is at the door, and he bade me bring
this to you. The callant is sair forfeuchen, and
in a lather o' sweat. He says he has run all the
way from Inverness, with a message to you from
the Dowager!"

Young Lady Macintosh sat up in bed, and
took the little tuft of feathers from her waiting-
maid's hand, examining it by the flickering light
of a candle.

"Yes, it comes from my mother-in-law," she
said, "and there must be something untoward
afoot, for her to send a laddie like Lachlan from
Inverness at this time of the morning."

Throwing a shawl round her shoulders, she hurried downstairs to where the tired boy was leaning against one of the big hall chairs. It needed but a glance to see how utterly spent and exhausted he was.

" The troops," he gasped, " the Sassenach troops. They are but two miles away. They are coming for the Prince."

" Are they, indeed?" said my lady calmly, for she was famed throughout the countryside for her extraordinary courage. " Then they'll perhaps have their own adoes to find him. Here, Walter, look to this bairn, and see that he has bite and sup, and a good sleep in a warm bed ; whilst thou, Hugh, run up to the Prince's chamber, and waken both him and his attendant. Go right in—this is no time for ceremony—and tell them to throw on their clothes, and to come here in the clap of a hand.

" Marget, help me to put up some bread and cheese and the paitricks that we roasted yesterday ; and Malcolm there can be ready to guide them up the burn to the cave in the side of the glen, where they can lie till all this stir be past and His Highness's own followers have time to come up."

Almost before the intrepid woman had finished speaking Prince Charlie was downstairs. He was a tall, handsome young man, with fair hair, blue eyes, and a fresh, ruddy complexion. He wore a short tartan coat, waistcoat, and kilt, also tartan hose and Highland brogues, and although he had dressed so rapidly, his clothes, though worn, were quite spick and span.

His eyes twinkled at the sight of his hostess's attire, but she allowed him no time for words. Putting the hastily prepared basket of provisions into his attendant's hands, and a warm plaid into his own, she let the two fugitives, accompanied by Malcolm, out of the house by a tiny postern door, telling them plainly and brusquely as she did so, that their lives depended on the speed with which they gained the cave and concealed themselves within its dark recesses.

When she had locked the door behind them, she went herself to the room that had been occupied by the Prince, and carefully removed anything that might point to its having been used within the last few weeks.

" I am going back to my bed now," she said, taking a last look round the apartment, " for if what young Lachlan said was true, Loudoun and his men must be near the front door now, and 'twere safer for them to find me just wakened out of sleep. 'Tis a wonder that Donald Fraser has not seen them coming. I have been afraid

of something like this, ever since I heard that
Cumberland's soldiers had arrived in Inverness.
So I dropped a word at the smiddy that it would
be well to keep a good look-out, and I fancy that
Donald and his friends have never slept in their
beds sinsyne."

"Aye, Donald has been out watching every
night, we ken that," replied the old porter; "but
he could but muster six men, and tho' they might
have given us notice that these English loons were
within hail, I canna see how they could have
done much more, for, if a' tales be true, it's a case
o' seven men against a thousand."

"Aweel, Donald has sense in his head, and
doubtless he knows his own plans best, and why
he has not warned us. I hardly think he would
be gowk* enough to let himself be taken prisoner.
But meanwhile I'll be off to my bed, and, when
they do arrive, see to it that the doors are
thrown open to them at once, and no obstacle
put in their way to prevent them searching the
house."

But the House o' Moy saw nothing of my Lord
of Loudoun and his troops that bright spring
morning.

For Donald Fraser the blacksmith was too
clever for them. 'Tis true he had only six men

* Fool.

under him, armed with ancient muskets which
no self - respecting soldier would have carried.
But he was a great strategian, and knew how
to make a little go a long way.

He had been up on the top of a hill, and had
heard the troops riding down the road on the
other side of it, when they were yet six miles away
from Moy.

So he had plenty of time to slip down the hill
again, and get his men stationed at long intervals
in a thick fir wood through which the road passed
as it neared the Castle. He not only placed them
where he meant them to stand, he told them in
what order he wanted them to fire, and what
battle-cries he wanted them to cry !

So when Loudoun's men came up, and their
leader, catching sight of the Castle through the
trees, gave orders to the piper (he was a Macleod,
who should have known better than to pipe to
English traitors) to give a skirl on his pipes, the
whole company was astonished and confused when
a shot rang out, and the piper, poor man, fell
in a heap on the road and never moved again.

They had little time for thought, however, for
shot after shot rang out of the wood, with here
a cry of " Come on, Macdonald !" and there a
cry of " Lochiel to the rescue !" and from the rear
came the slogan of the Mackinnons, while in the

forefront the dauntless smith made the wood ring with the names of the Ogilvies and Macphersons.

Queer, fantastic figures jumped out from among the trees—or so the soldiers said, when they were safe back in Inverness, and had gathered their wits—and laid on to both men and horse with great clubs, which, after all, must just have been the butts of the ancient muskets, after their owners' powder was finished.

Anyhow, it was a laughable story, and right ashamed of it the English were for many a long day.

For the horses that were in front reared, and their riders, scared out of their senses, let them turn and run into the ranks behind them. And the men in these ranks did the same, until everything was in confusion and nobody knew what was happening, or how many men were attacking them, or how many more were coming on. In vain Lord Loudoun shouted and raved, trying to rally the cowards and to get some kind of order. He might as well have cried to the moon. A perfect panic had seized his men, and it was a case of "every man for himself, and the deil take the hindmost."

Along the road back to Inverness they clattered, casting fearful looks over their shoulders as they did so, to see how many Highlanders were behind them. And it was not till they were gathered together and drawn up in the square of the little town, at eleven o'clock the next forenoon, that they learned from the jeers of the crowd, and the fearsome language with which their commander vented his wrath on their heads, that they had been completely routed by seven brave men, and that they had missed their opportunity, for the Prince's followers had come up in such numbers that there was no chance of them being able to outwit them again.

Printed by offset in Great Britain by
Billing and Sons Ltd , Guildford and Esher